KNOW YOUR SPORT 2 QUIZ BOOK

GW00569754

KNOW YOUR SPORT 2

QUIZ BOOK

with
George Hamilton

GILL AND MACMILLAN
AND
RADIO TELEFÍS ÉIREANN

Published by
Gill and Macmillan Ltd
Goldenbridge
Dublin 8
and
Radio Telefís Éireann
Donnybrook
Dublin 4
© RTE 1992
0 7171 2028 7
Cover photograph by
Ronnie Norton Studios Ltd
Print origination by
Seton Music Graphics Ltd, Bantry, Co. Cork
Printed by Colour Books Ltd, Dublin

A catalogue record is available for this book from the
British Library.

Know Your Sport was
conceived and devised for
television by Mary Hogan.

Introduction

When we launched the first *Know Your Sport Quiz Book* in 1991, we knew that there was a demand for it among our viewers. What we didn't know was just how big that demand was. But you bought it in such numbers that we were all both surprised and delighted. So, we've decided to do another one — and here it is.

This year sees *Know Your Sport* back for its sixth season in the familiar Monday evening slot at 7 o'clock. The programme goes from strength to strength and continues to hold a high place in the audience ratings. Thankfully, there's no shortage of sports-mad viewers out there!

Nor is there any shortage of outstanding competitors. All *Know Your Sport* competitors are stars. It's not just the winners who make the show but everyone who competes and puts their sporting knowledge on the line. It isn't always easy, under the glare of the television lights, to have those answers on the tip of your tongue. It's one thing to know the answer; it's another thing altogether to remember it when you're under pressure.

So when you're playing *Know Your Sport* at home and beating our contestants, don't forget that it isn't as easy as it looks. The studio pressure is real: although the show is recorded, it's done straight through in a single take. So as far as the contestants are concerned, they are on live television.

For you, it's easier. But you can get some idea of what it's like if you play the game with the *Know Your Sport 2 Quiz Book*. Try these questions against the clock. You'll find that they are fun — but challenging fun!

Good luck!

GEORGE HAMILTON

Questions

1. Traditionally, which is the first of the annual Majors?

2. How many entries were there for the first British Open in 1860?

3. What is Jack Nicklaus's middle name?

4. Which Irish golfer returned to the pro circuit in April 1992, following a three-year lay-off due to a serious car accident?

5. A record number of Europeans played the 1992 US Masters. How many?

6. Who won the inaugural World Match Play Championship in 1964?

7. Who in 1938 was the first Irish player to play in the Curtis Cup?

8. How much did the winner of the 1930 British Open receive?

9. The 1991 Ryder Cup was staged at Kiawah Island. In what US state is this course?

10. On which course is the 126-yard hole known as the 'postage stamp'?

11. What was the highest place achieved by Christy O'Connor Snr in the British Open?

12. On which course is Rae's Creek encountered?

13. Who won the British Open in both 1949 and 1950?

14. Which famous British venue has two courses, Ailsa and Arran?

15. Who in 1983 became the first Japanese player to achieve a US PGA Tour victory?

Answers on page 69

1. Who won his third Carroll's Irish Open in 1986?

2. Who was the first English golfer to gross £100,000 on the European Tour?

3. Who was the victorious European captain of the 1985 Ryder Cup?

4. Who holed from a bunker to deny Greg Norman victory in the 1986 US PGA Championship?

5. Which country retained the Dunhill Cup in 1986?

6. Name the 1992 US Masters Champion.

7. What event was initially sponsored by Piccadilly, later by Colgate and currently by Suntory?

8. The film *Follow the Sun* was based on the life of which golfer?

9. In which year did Greg Norman win his first Australian Open?

10. Which year saw the oldest winners (up to 1992) of the US Master and Open titles?

11. Who in 1981 became the first Australian to win the US Open?

12. Which three holes on the Masters course at Augusta are known as 'Amen Corner'?

13. Who in 1953 won the US Masters, the US Open and the British Open?

14. How many times was Joe Carr British Amateur Champion?

15. Up to 1992 how many Majors has Jack Nicklaus won as a professional?

Answers on page 69

1. Which was the first year in which the British Open was officially scheduled to end on a Sunday?

2. Who up to 1991 has been the only Japanese winner of the World Matchplay Championship?

3. Which Irish player won the 1957 Ladies' British Open Amateur title?

4. At what age did Severiano Ballesteros win his first British Open Championship in 1979?

5. Which golfer designed the Muirfield, Ohio course?

6. Name the world's oldest golfing society founded in England in 1898 and without a course of its own.

7. When was the rule limiting the number of clubs to fourteen imposed in both Britain and the USA?

8. Who did Nick Faldo defeat at the second extra hole in the 1989 US Masters?

9. Where did Ireland achieve its historic Canada Cup (now World Cup) victory in 1958?

10. Which British Open provided Greg Norman with his first Major?

11. The winner's purse for the 1863 British Open was £10 and had risen to £1,500 by 1963. What was it in 1983?

12. True or false: the Ryder Cup is an older competition than the Walker Cup?

13. Where was the 1991 Carroll's Irish Open staged?

14. Name the trophy awarded annually by the PGA to the leading player in the Order of Merit.

15. Who was leading money winner on the 1970 European PGA Tour?

Answers on page 70

1. The US lost the 1933 Ryder Cup. When were they next defeated in the event?

2. In which country is Tuctu Golf Club where putts drop at 14,335 feet?

3. Which European golfer had successive victories in the Japanese Open Championship in 1977–78?

4. Who in 1979 was the first European golfer to win the European Open?

5. Which Ulster club hosted the 1968 Curtis Cup on the first occasion the event was staged in Ireland?

6. Joe Carr played 157 matches for Ireland. How many did he win?

7. Who holed in one during round one of the 1979 British Open at Royal Lytham?

8. Which company sponsors golf's World-ranking List?

9. Whose six World Cup appearances between 1960 and 1967 were all on a winning team?

10. Which European golfer was disqualified for arriving late on tee at the 1980 US Open?

11. Which eighteen-year-old won the 1982 Venezuelan Open?

12. Which country, rated as complete outsiders, defeated England in round one of the 1986 Dunhill Nations Cup?

13. Who, having finished second in the 1984 British Open, went on to capture both the Dutch and Carroll's Irish Open within two weeks?

Answers on page 70

1. Name the Australian golfer who in 1973, became the first non-American to top $1 million earnings on the US PGA Tour.

2. Who receives the 'Old Claret Jug'?

3. At which course in the 1985 British Open did Christy O'Connor Jnr shoot a record round of sixty-four?

4. Where was the 1991 Walker Cup played?

5. Who had a fifteen-year span between his victory in 1959 and his next British Open success?

6. Who was runaway winner of the 1987 Irish Open at Portmarnock?

7. Which year saw the first £1,000 winner's cheque and first live TV coverage of the British Open?

8. Fred Daly won the 1947 British Open. Which Irish golfer finished second in 1948 and third in the 1950 and '52 event?

9. In 1969 which English course hosted the first Ryder Cup match to end in a tie?

10. By what name was Liang-Huan known to golfing fans when he was runner-up in the 1971 British Open?

11. Which is the world's oldest Men's Amateur Championship?

12. Name the three Irish players on the victorious 1986 Great Britain and Ireland Curtis Cup team.

13. Who represented Argentina fifteen times and Mexico four in the Canada and World Cups?

14. Which US professional topped $4 million in gross career earnings when finishing sixth in the 1983 Bing Crosby Pro-Am?

Answers on page 71

1. Who defeated Greg Norman in a play-off to win the 1984 US Open?

2. Who won seven Australian Open Championships between 1958 and 1974?

3. Who in 1990 repeated his 1987 success in the Suntory World Matchplay Championship?

4. In which year was the Dunhill Nations Cup inaugurated?

5. Which US golfer ignored a death threat and won the 1977 US Open?

6. Who won the 1986 Panasonic Las Vegas Invitational, where for the first time in a tournament, the winner's purse exceeded $200,000?

7. Ireland won its first men's 'home' International Championship outright in 1950. When did they next win it?

8. Which four-times winner of the British Open was charged with attempted murder in 1979?

9. Why was there a late switch in venue — Muirfield to St Andrews in the 1957 British Open?

10. Who is the annual recipient of the Tooting Bec Cup?

11. Which Irish golfer captured the men's 1946 British Amateur title?

12. Who was the first golfer to win the British Boys' Championship (1983), British Amateur Championship (1984) and the British Youth's Championship (1985)?

13. On which English championship course are the holes Turnberry, Ailsa and Well located?

Answers on page 71

1. Who was 1978 winner of the Carroll's Irish Open?

2. Which overseas player set a course record of sixty-three in the 1986 Masters at Augusta?

3. When winning the British Open in 1868, 'Young' Tom Morris set a record which still remains. What record is this?

4. Who in 1986 was voted both Australia's Sportsman of the Year and the BBC Overseas Sports Personality of the Year?

5. Who in the 1970 US Open was the first winner to lead from round one as well as the only player to break par in that year?

6. Who was World Seniors Champion in both 1976 and '77?

7. Whose six victories on the 1986 PGA Tour included the Dunhill British Masters, the Carroll's Irish and the Dutch and French Open Championships?

8. Who made nine consecutive Curtis Cup appearances for Great Britain and Ireland between 1970 and 1986?

9. How many consecutive Ryder Cup appearances did Christy O'Connor Snr make between 1955 and 1973?

10. At which course in 1947 did Fred Daly achieve Ireland's only success up to 1992, in the British Open Championship?

11. Where did Belfast-born Sam (Max) McCready win the 1949 British Amateur title?

12. Whom did Larry Mize defeat in a play-off for the 1987 US Masters?

Answers on page 72

1. Who won the 1983 Embassy World Professional Championship?

2. What is the minimum number of darts required to complete a game of 1,001?

3. Who was inaugural winner of the Men's World Professional Championship in 1978?

4. England suffered a defeat by which unlikely country in the 1978 Nations Cup?

5. In which year did Eric Bristow win his first Embassy World Professional Championship?

6. Which country won the 1977 inaugural World Cup?

7. Who in 1979 was the first player 'whitewashed' in an Embassy World Professional Championship Final?

8. Who in 1978 became the first non-British player to win the *News of the World* Championship?

9. Who was the inaugural winner of the Men's British Professional Championship in 1981?

10. Which player in 1984 achieved the first nine-dart finish (for 501) in a major World Matchplay event?

11. What are the numbers on either side of 13 on a regulation dartboard?

12. Whose scalp did Irishman Steve Brennan claim in the first round of the 1982 Embassy World Professional Championship?

13. Who was the first player to win the four major world titles: World Masters (1976), Embassy World Professional Championship (1979), World Cup Singles (1981) and *News of the World* Championship (1981)?

Answers on page 72

1. In which country did the game originate in 1875?

2. Who won the 1992 Benson and Hedges Irish Masters?

3. Who was the first winner of the UK Professional Championship in 1977?

4. Who took the 1989 Embassy World Championship Final by eighteen frames to three?

5. Who succeeded Joe Davis as World Professional Champion in 1947?

6. Ray Reardon won BBC TV's first 'Pot Black' competition in 1969. Who won the last event in 1986?

7. Who was 1989 World Amateur Champion?

8. The Langs Scottish Masters ran from 1981–87. Who won the title on three successive occasions?

9. How many players constitute a team in snooker's World Cup?

10. Which player registered four centuries against Alex Higgins in a 1986 Embassy World Professional match?

11. Who was the first player to retain his Embassy World title at the Crucible?

12. In which year was the first *official* century break recorded?

13. Which 1985 final was the first to offer a winner's prize of £50,000?

14. In which city was Stephen Hendry born in 1969?

15. John Spencer, winner of the first Benson and Hedges Irish Masters in 1978, beat the 1979 winner in the final. Who was he?

Answers on page 72

1. The 1985 Embassy World Champion also won the 1984–85 Rothman's Grand Prix. Who was he?

2. Which city housed the last Embassy World Professional Championship before it moved to its permanent location at the Crucible, in 1977?

3. Which player at the age of sixty-six added the 1980 World Professional Billiards title to an impressive snooker record?

4. Where is the venue of the British Benson and Hedges Masters?

5. To whom did defending champion Steve Davis lose 10–1 in the first round of the 1982 Embassy World Championship?

6. How did the Lada Classic of 1982 enter the record books?

7. Name the Canadian player fined £10,000 for drug abuse during the 1985 British Open.

8. The 1980 winner of the Embassy World Championship received £15,000. What did the 1989 winner receive?

9. Who in 1927 was the first Professional World Champion?

10. Which debutant won the 1972 Embassy World Championship?

11. Who was Canadian Professional Champion from 1984–87 inclusive?

12. Up to 1992 how many Irish players have won the Benson and Hedges Irish Masters?

13. What did Cliff Thorburn achieve on 23 April 1983?

Answers on page 73

1. What is the minimum length of a cue?

2. What was the nationality of Perrie Mans, beaten finalist in the 1978 Embassy World Professional Final?

3. In which year did Steve Davis win the first of his Benson and Hedges Irish Masters titles?

4. What sets Perrie Mans and Dean Reynolds apart from the vast majority of their fellow professionals?

5. How many Embassy World titles has Steve Davis won up to 1992?

6. In what city was Tony Meo born in 1959?

7. Who up to 1992 is the oldest player to appear in the Embassy World Professional Championship Final?

8. Which two players battling for a 1985 crown provided the BBC with an audience of 18.5 m — a record for a domestic sporting event?

9. Who in 1980 defeated Alex Higgins 16–6 for the first of his UK Professional titles?

10. Name the repeat pairing who contested the 1987 Embassy World Championship Final.

11. Who defeated Dennis Taylor in the 1979 Embassy World Professional Championship Final?

12. The World Doubles Championships ran from 1982–87. Who partnered Steve Davis to four victories?

13. Who won the 1990 Embassy World Professional Championship?

14. Who took the 1990 World Amateur title?

15. When was the current snooker scoring system introduced: 1891, 1919 or 1933?

Answers on page 73

1. In which European League do Anderlecht play?

2. Which German prisoner-of-war remained in England to become one of the country's leading goalkeepers?

3. In which year did Arsenal and Liverpool first meet in an FA Cup Final?

4. How may a club gain automatic entry to the European Cup?

5. Who in 1956 were first winners of the European Cup?

6. Which soccer star claimed in 1968 that he 'wouldn't kiss any girl if she smoked too much'?

7. Who was nicknamed the 'Flying Plumber'?

8. In which Scottish city do St Johnstone play?

9. Which country staged the 1970 World Cup Finals?

10. Who was England's Footballer of the Year in the 1966–67 season?

11. Who receives the *Copa Libertadores*?

12. How many times was Billy Wright capped for England between 1946 and 1959?

13. Whom did Barclays select as their 1991 'Young Eagle of the Year'?

14. Whose autobiography appeared in 1991 as *Frankly Speaking*?

15. Name the Englishman who became FIFA President in 1961.

Answers on page 74

1. Which English club plays in the Scottish League?

2. Who was the last player signed by Jock Stein for Celtic?

3. How many Football League clubs did Tom Finney play for during a long and distinguished career?

4. Who was the only Republic of Ireland manager of an English First Division club during the 1970–71 season?

5. Who were the first winners of the English Division One title in the 20th century?

6. Cardiff City took the FA Cup to Wales in 1927. Who were the defeated finalists?

7. What popular football competition introduced in the *Athletic News* on 30 April 1928 still features on the sports pages?

8. At which English ground in 1946 were thirty-three killed and over 500 injured following the collapse of two barriers?

9. Who scored a hat-trick for Hungary in their 1963 Wembley defeat of England?

10. Name the Chairman of the Professional Footballer's Association when the minimum wage was abolished.

11. Geoff Hurst scored a hat-trick, but who scored England's other goal in their 4–2 World Cup victory over Germany in 1966?

12. Who succeeded Tommy Docherty as Manchester United manager?

13. Dean Court is the home ground of which English club?

Answers on page 74

1. Who collected his hundredth English Cap during the 1988 European Championships?

2. Who scored Ireland's winner against Morocco in Dublin on 12 September 1990?

3. The nickname of which English team resembles the name of an ancient city destroyed in 79 AD?

4. Which Real Madrid star of the 1960s was nicknamed the 'White Arrow'?

5. Which Irish League side was knocked out of the 1970–71 European Cup by a League of Ireland club?

6. Who scored four goals for Birmingham City in his tenth appearance for the club when still only sixteen years of age?

7. What was the exact date of the Manchester United Munich disaster?

8. What money-spinning gimmick did Englishman John Moores introduce in 1923?

9. At which ground in 1947 did 134,000 see Great Britain defeat the Rest of Europe 6–1?

10. Who were the first country to defeat England abroad?

11. Which player was transferred from Stoke City to Blackpool for £12,000 in May 1947?

12. Who captained Liverpool to 1965 FA Cup victory?

13. Name the 1970 World Cup finalists.

14. Who was sacked as Manchester United manager on 4 July 1977?

15. Who was Liverpool's manager at the time of the Heysel disaster?

Answers on page 75

1. Who scored six times for Manchester United in a fifth round cup tie versus Northampton in the 1969–70 season?

2. With which four English League clubs did Billy Bingham play?

3. Which English international was nicknamed the 'Lion of Vienna'?

4. What have Edu (1984–85), Santana (1985–86), Lazaroni (1989–90) and Falcao (1990–91), particularly in common?

5. Millmoor Ground is the home of which English club nicknamed the 'Merry Millers'?

6. Which organisation was founded in Manchester on 2 December 1907?

7. What rule change introduced at the beginning of the 1925–26 season was expected to revolutionise football?

8. Who are 'The Mariners' whose home ground is at Blundell Park?

9. Who was Manchester United's manager immediately before Tommy Docherty?

10. Of which English Third Division club did Eoin Hand become manager in 1988?

11. Which team in 1910 conceded home advantage in their FA Cup draw for £1,000 and lost the 'away' game 4–2 to Bradford City?

12. Why is Thursday 29 June 1950 recorded as 'the blackest day in English football'?

13. Against which team did Joe Payne (Luton Town) score ten goals on Easter Monday 1936?

Answers on page 75

1. Who won the 1982 European Cup?

2. Which English club began life in 1880 as St Mark's, West Gorton, becoming Gorton in 1884 and Ardwick in 1887 before adopting their present name in 1894?

3. Who managed Coventry City from 1961 to 1967?

4. Which player was signed for £5 m on 28 May 1982?

5. England defeated Argentina 3–1 on 17 May 1980, but which team scored a historic 4–1 victory over England four days later?

6. Scores by Brooking and McCluskey ensured cross-channel Cup success for which two clubs in 1980?

7. Which club's home ground is at Douglas Park, Hamilton?

8. Who scored all England's goals in their 4–2 victory over Spain on 18 February 1987?

9. From which club did Coventry City purchase Robert Rosario in March 1991?

10. Who won the first post-war FA Cup?

11. Who knocked Manchester United out of the 1990–91 FA Cup?

12. Name the Smirnoff 1990–91 Irish League winners.

13. Who completed the 1988 Scottish League and Cup double?

14. Which former Republic of Ireland international managed Oxford United for a brief period in 1988?

15. Which judge led the inquiry into the 1989 Hillsborough Disaster?

Answers on page 76

1. Where did Poland draw 3–3 with Ireland on 16 October 1991?

2. Which club took the European Cup in 1974, '75 and '76?

3. Up to the 1992–93 season how many times have Arsenal won the FA Cup?

4. Which team took the place of Workington in the Fourth Division of the Football League in the 1977–78 season?

5. Who took over as Liverpool's caretaker manager following the resignation of Kenny Dalglish?

6. Which club had the highest average attendance (39,077) for the 1990–91 English League season?

7. Name Ireland's penalty-takers in the dramatic 1990 World Cup shoot-out with Romania.

8. Name the official history of Liverpool FC published in 1987.

9. As of May 1992, who is the only Irish player with exactly fifty international caps?

10. Which soccer manager commented in 1964: 'I've got no room for shirkers. I want a man who'll go through a wall of fire, break a leg and still come out shooting for goal'?

11. Against which opponents did John Aldridge notch his first international hat-trick?

12. Which country lost 5–2 to Brazil in the 1958 World Cup Final?

13. Sir Alf Ramsey, Bobby Robson, Bobby Ferguson and John Lyall have all managed which English League club?

Answers on page 76

1. In 1901, the FA Cup was won by a non-League side, the only time that this has happened. Who were the winners?

2. Which was the first FA Cup Final to be broadcast on radio?

3. Name the 1954–55 Division One Champions prevented from playing in the European Cup by express order of the English Football League.

4. Which player was transferred from Leeds to Juventus for a (then) record fee of £70,000 in 1957?

5. Who were the Spurs players responsible for six of the goals in England's 1961 victory over Scotland by 9 goals to 3?

6. Who was Sunderland's manager in their 1973 defeat of favourites Leeds United in the 1973 FA Cup Final?

7. Who beat Rangers 1–0 after extra time in the 1983 Scottish Cup Final?

8. In the 1982 World Cup Final who scored Germany's consolation goal in reply to Italy's three?

9. Who beat Spain 2–0 to take the 1984 European Championship?

10. From which Italian club was Graeme Souness signed as Glasgow Rangers player-manager in 1986?

11. To which English club was St Patrick's Athletic player Curtis Fleming transferred in 1991?

12. Up to the 1992–93 season which club has won the Scottish Cup twenty-nine times?

13. Which team finished runners-up to Dundalk in the 1990–91 League of Ireland?

Answers on page 77

1. Who was the first player to notch a hat-trick for Ireland under Jack Charlton?

2. Name the book by Stephen McGarrigle which deals with Arsenal's Irish players.

3. Who was England's 1990–91 Footballer of the Year?

4. How many goals did Liverpool concede in forty-two games when winning the 1978–79 First Division Championship?

5. Which soccer manager in 1978, when asked his opinion of a certain official, commented: 'Call that man a coach? I'd call him a hearse'?

6. Who resigned as England manager in July 1977?

7. What was the Rumbelows Cup originally called?

8. Which country took the 1976 European Championship 5–3 on penalties?

9. Up to the 1992–93 season four clubs have each made eleven English FA Cup Final appearances. Name three of them.

10. Who managed Limerick City in their 1991–92 First Division Championship success?

11. Which BBC commentator wrote the *Official History of the Football League 1888–1988*?

12. Who in 1960 were first winners of the World Club Championship?

13. At what age did Sir Stanley Matthews play his 710th — and last — competitive game against Fulham on 6 February 1965?

Answers on page 77

1. Which club defeated Glasgow Celtic after a play-off in the 1967 World Club Championship?

2. Which manager, having been sacked by Atletico Madrid commented: 'You'd think taking a club from eighteenth to third in three months was good enough'?

3. Who in November 1978 became the first black player to represent England at full international level?

4. Name Manchester United's captain in their 1968 European Cup win.

5. Which Scottish team are nicknamed 'The Bankies'?

6. Where did Chelsea and Leeds United replay their drawn 1970 FA Cup Final?

7. Which team defeated Group Five table-toppers Northern Ireland 4–1 in the next round of the 1982 World Cup?

8. By what score did the Republic of Ireland beat Malta in their 16 November 1983 meeting in Dublin?

9. Who in 1985 won the 100th Scottish Cup Final?

10. Who were runners-up to Aston Villa for the 1980–81 Division One title?

11. Tannadice Park is home ground to which Scottish club?

12. Which club's FA Cup wins have been in the seasons 1909–10, 1923–24, 1931–32, 1950–51 and 1954–55?

13. Which two English First Division clubs are subject of the book *Heroes and Villains 1990–91 Season*?

14. Which was the first FAI Cup Final to be televised live?

Answers on page 78

1. Who up to June 1992 is the only Irish player to be sent off under Jack Charlton's tenure as manager?

2. Which two goalkeepers were successive English Footballers of the Year in 1971–72 and 1972–73?

3. Who up to the 1991–92 season is the Irish team physio?

4. For which two English clubs did Scotland's Bobby Collins play?

5. How much did Italian League club Bari pay for David Platt in July 1991?

6. Who was Barclay's Manager of the Year 1990–91?

7. Which Manchester United player said in 1967: 'When I'm on the field nothing gives me more pleasure than making a fool of somebody'?

8. England scored seven goals in qualifying matches for the 1992 European Championships. How many did Ireland score?

9. Who won the first Woman's World Cup in Canton, China, in November 1991?

10. Who defeated reigning champions Argentina 1–0 in the opening round of the 1982 World Cup?

11. Who scored twice for Tottenham Hotspur in their 3–2 defeat of Manchester City in the replayed 1981 FA Cup Final?

12. In which year did Bill Shankly die?

13. Which footballer's autobiography is entitled *Macca'can*?

14. Which English League local derby would have the 'Robins' and 'Pirates' in opposition?

Answers on page 78

1. How many points are awarded for a conversion?

2. Out of which city do the 'Raiders' play?

3. Where did the New York Jets move to in 1984?

4. How many Superbowls have there been to April 1992?

5. Out of which city do the Seahawks play?

6. Who would be the opposing sides in a 'Cowboys' v 'Chiefs' game?

7. How many players may a team have on field during play?

8. Which word describes an accumulation or loss of yards?

9. From which city are the 'Eagles'?

10. What in team formation do the letters LT abbreviate?

11. Mile High Stadium is in which city?

12. Which word describes the grouping of players between 'downs' at which the next strategy is set?

13. Which team is at home at Sullivan Stadium?

14. How many officials police the on-field game?

15. Name Super Bowl XXV winners.

Answers on page 79

1. What car did Giuseppe Farina drive to victory in the inaugural World Championships in 1950?

2. Who up to 1992 has been the youngest winner of the World Formula One Driver's Championship?

3. What was the nationality of racing driver Jody Scheckter?

4. Who took the 1982 Formula One World Driver's Championship?

5. What car won the 1983 Formula One Constructor's Cup?

6. How many Grand Prix wins did Alain Prost have in the 1980s?

7. What car did John Watson drive on the circuit from 1981–83?

8. In which country was the 1980 Formula One World Champion Alan Jones, born?

9. Who returned after a near fatal crash in 1976 to take Formula One World Championships in 1977 and 1984?

10. Which English driver took the 1976 Formula One World Championship?

11. What car did Nelson Piquet drive to 1981 Formula One World Championship success?

12. How many times was Stirling Moss runner-up in the World Formula One Driver's Championship?

13. He died on 14 August 1988 having seen the company he founded amass thirteen world titles in forty-eight years. Who was he?

Answers on page 79

1. Which country won the first Three-Day Event World Championship in 1966?

2. Where were the 1991 European Three-Day Event Championships held?

3. Who rode Glenburnie to victory in the 1991 European Men's Three-Day Event?

4. Graham Fletcher is associated with which horse named after the Co. Cork town where the famous Cahirmee Fair is held annually?

5. Which Irish rider won the first Hickstead Derby in 1961?

6. Who are current sponsors of the Nations Cup which is competed for in specific events internationally?

7. Name the Austrian rider who took the first Individual Showjumping World Cup title in 1979.

8. Who rode Pele to Silver Medal position in the 1974 World Individual Showjumping Championship?

9. Name the founder of Millstreet International Show.

10. What is the first competition of the Three-Day Event?

11. Which Irish rider won the 1975 Hickstead Derby?

12. What was Boomerang renamed?

13. Up to 1991, when did Ireland last win the European Three-Day Event title?

14. Which Olympic Games introduced the first full equestrian programme?

15. On which horse did Ireland's Seamus Hayes twice win the Hickstead Derby?

Answers on page 80

1. Which versatile US player won three of his five US Opens (1974–83) on different surfaces?

2. Whose mentor is Wojtek Fibak?

3. Whom did John McEnroe defeat in the 1983 Wimbledon Final?

4. Who, after losing the 1989 US Women's Final to Steffi Graf, commented: 'I know how to beat her, I just wasn't able to do it'?

5. How many Wimbledon Singles titles did Chris Evert win?

6. Who was 'Little Mo' who achieved the first Women's Grand Slam in 1953?

7. Which country won the Davis Cup for the first time in 1980?

8. Who took the US Men's Singles title in 1985, '86, '87?

9. In which country was Miloslav Mecir born?

10. Who in 1977 was the last English player to take the Ladies' Singles title at Wimbledon?

11. In which country was John McEnroe born?

12. Which two creatures stopped play at the 1989 Wimbledon Championships?

13. Who took the 1987 Men's Singles title at Wimbledon?

14. Who partnered fellow Swede Joakim Nystrom in taking the 1986 Men's Doubles title at Wimbledon?

15. Paraguay caused a real upset in 1987 when eliminating which nation from the Davis Cup?

Answers on page 80

1. Who was the 1991 winner of the Men's French Open Championship?

2. Who was the defending Ladies' Singles Champion at Wimbledon in 1992?

3. Who lost four US Men's Singles Finals between 1976 and 1981?

4. Who in 1938 was the first man to achieve the Grand Slam?

5. Which fifteen-year-old US girl became in 1980 the youngest seeded player in the history of Wimbledon?

6. Who was the inaugural winner of the Men's ATP Tour World Championship in 1990?

7. From which countries were the 1991 Wimbledon, US and French Doubles Champions J. Fitzgerald and A. Jarryd?

8. Which Hollywood actor walked out of the Royal Box at Wimbledon because of embarrassment at John McEnroe's Centre Court antics?

9. Who in 1920 was the first player to take all three available Wimbledon titles?

10. Prior to the 1989 Wimbledon Championships which player paid a £100,000 insurance premium for a £6 m payout in the event of kidnap?

11. Which former Wimbledon Champion wed Italian pop star Loredana Berte in September 1989?

12. Which defeated Wimbledon finalist commented in 1989: 'This isn't my last stand. I'm not Custer'?

13. In which year were the first All-England Championships held at Wimbledon?

Answers on page 81

1. When did Sean Kelly win the first of his seven consecutive Paris-Nice Classics?

2. Which French rider won the 1978 and '79 Tour de France?

3. In which year were the World Professional Road Championships first held?

4. In which country did the 1987 Tour de France start?

5. Who in 1989 became the first British winner in the eighty-one year history of the Tour of Belgium?

6. Sean Kelly took the points classification in the 1989 Tour de France. Who was runner-up?

7. Who won the Tour de France from 1969–72 inclusive?

8. Is the Tour of Britain Milk Race an amateur, professional or 'mixed' event?

9. The Olympic 1,000 Metre Time Trial was introduced at the 1896 Games. When did a Russian cyclist win the event?

10. What significance had Benemide in the 1988 Tour de France?

11. Over whom had Greg Le Mond a mere eight-second victory in the 1989 Tour de France?

12. What is the amateur equivalent of the Tour de France?

13. Up to 1991, how many Irish cyclists have won the Tour of Britain Milk Race?

14. Who lost three minutes through signing autographs at the Luxembourg start of the 1989 Tour de France?

15. Maurice Garin (France) won the first Tour de France in which year?

Answers on page 81

1. Which university was Sonia O'Sullivan representing when breaking the 1,500 m Indoor world record in 1991?

2. Who took the gold medal in the Women's Marathon at the Seoul Olympics?

3. At which Olympic Games were electric timing and photo-finish equipment first introduced?

4. Where were the 1991 World Track and Field Championships staged?

5. Which women's event did the Heptathlon replace at the 1984 Los Angeles Olympics?

6. What special way is the Olympic flame kindled at Mount Olympus?

7. How many World Cross Country titles did former Olympic Champion Gaston Roelants win?

8. Which barefoot athlete took the 1960 Olympic Marathon title?

9. Where did the number of track and field athletes exceed 1,000 for the first time at an Olympic Games?

10. Who has broken the World Pole Vault record nine times since 1984?

11. In which year did Roger Bannister crash the four-minute-mile barrier?

12. As of August 1992, whose 1979 Men's 200 m world record remained unbroken?

13. Which Irish athlete won the 1991 World Cup Hill Running Championship in Zermatt, Switzerland?

14. What was the nationality of the Marathon winner at the first Modern Olympics in Athens in 1896?

Answers on page 82

1. Which athlete completed the Men's 800 m and 1,500 m double at the Tokyo Olympics?

2. Which Games introduced the practice of bringing the Olympic Flame from Mount Olympus in Greece to the Olympic arena?

3. Who was the first athlete to break 3:50 for the Mile?

4. Who set a new Men's world record in the Long Jump at the 1991 World Track and Field Championships?

5. Where in 1958 did Herb Elliott smash Derek Ibbotson's 3:57.2 World Mile record?

6. Name the 1991 winner of the BLE Men's National Half-Marathon in Cork.

7. Which country won the 4 x 400 m Men's Relay at the 1991 World Track and Field Championships?

8. Which picturesque resort hosts the annual NFC All-Ireland Triathlon?

9. Who won the inaugural Women's Marathon at the 1984 Olympics?

10. Which former President of the International Olympic Committee commented in 1956: 'The 880-yard heel and toe walk is the closest a man can come to experiencing the pangs of childbirth'?

11. Who were 1980 Olympic Ice Hockey Champions?

12. Who defeated Catherine McKiernan in the 1992 World Cross Country Championships?

13. Who played the 1912 dual US Olympic Champion Jim Thorpe on screen in *Man of Bronze*?

Answers on page 82

1. As of August 1992, seven Irish names appear in the top ten World Fastest Indoor Mile list. Name three of the four different athletes involved.

2. Which nation finished as leading medal winners at the 1991 World Track and Field Championships?

3. Which Irish athlete took the gold medal in the Men's 1,500 m at the 1991 World Student Games?

4. Who are current sponsors of the Dublin City Marathon?

5. How many athletes broke the 10 second barrier in the 1988 Men's Olympic 100 m Final?

6. Which athlete won the gold medal following the Zola Budd-Mary Decker incident in the 1984 Olympic 3,000 m Final?

7. How many nations participated in the 1896 Athens Olympic Games?

8. Which athlete finally broke Jesse Owens' world record Long Jump which had stood for some twenty-five years?

9. Who won the 1960 Men's Olympic 1,500 m Final by twenty yards?

10. During the 1956 Olympic Games athletes from which country tore down the Communist Party flag over their headquarters, replacing it with their native flag?

11. Six of the top ten fastest Miles have all been run in which city?

12. How many obstacles or barriers face the athletes in a 3,000 m Steeplechase event?

13. Who succeeded Bruce Jenner as Olympic Decathlon Champion?

Answers on page 82

1. Which athlete completed his second successive Olympic double 5,000/10,000 m at the 1976 Olympic Games in Montreal?

2. What enabled the 1964 Tokyo Olympic Games to be watched by the biggest ever live TV audience?

3. Name one of the athletes expelled from the US team for giving the Black Power salute during the medal ceremony at the Mexico Olympics.

4. Which 1932 Olympic swimming champion later played both Buck Rogers and Flash Gordon on screen?

5. Whose world record 3:49.78 for the Indoor Mile set in 1983, was still unbeaten in August 1992?

6. Who took the Women's 10,000 m at the 1991 World Track and Field Championships?

7. Who took the gold medal in the Women's 1,500 m at the 1991 World Student Games?

8. Where since 1973 have the Irish National Community Games been held?

9. Which US athlete retained his 110 m Hurdles title at the 1988 Olympics?

10. Percy Hodge won the event in Antwerp. Which athlete bridged a thirty-six-year gap when winning the 3,000 m Steeplechase for Britain at the Melbourne Olympics of 1956?

11. Which athlete won Britain's first gold medal in the Women's Javelin at Los Angeles in 1984?

12. Name Britain's first female Olympic Track gold medallist.

Answers on page 83

1. Which country won the Men's 4 x 100 m Relay at the Seoul Olympics?

2. Who was the first British pole-vaulter to clear 18 ft?

3. An athlete from which country won the Men's Marathon at the 1991 World Track and Field Championships?

4. Which Irish athlete won four gold medals at the 1991 World Veteran Track and Field Championships in Turku, Finland?

5. Who was Ireland's gold medal winner in the 1991 Men's 3,000 m at the World Indoor Championships?

6. Prior to John Walker, which New Zealander broke the World Mile record in 1962 and '64?

7. Which woman sprinter completed the 100 m/200 m double at the 1991 World Track and Field Championships?

8. Which athlete said: 'I was not invited to shake hands with Hitler, but I was not invited to the White House to shake hands with the President either'?

9. Which modern Olympics introduced the gold medal?

10. Which athlete in 1973 achieved the first World Record in the High Jump using the 'Fosbury Flop' technique?

11. Which Marathon on 1 November 1987 had a record 21,141 finishers?

12. Why was there such a dramatic improvement in pole-vault performances in the early 1960s?

13. Which Olympic Games introduced the three-tiered victory rostrum with its accompanying anthem and flag-raising?

Answers on page 83

1. Of whom was former British Olympic star Alan Wells speaking in 1989 when he said: 'I wouldn't be surprised if one day his halo slipped and choked him'?

2. Who won the Men's 5,000 m at the 1988 Olympic Games?

3. What in 1989 was the 'Woo-Woo'?

4. In which country is Admira Wacker a successful football club?

5. With which sport are the teams Essendon, Fitzroy and Collingwood especially associated?

6. Who took the Men's 3,000 m event at the 1989 World Indoor Championships?

7. Which football team won the 1979 European Cup, defeating Malmo 1–0 in the Final?

8. In which year did Shergar win the Epsom Derby?

9. Who in 1958 was the first teenager to run a sub-four-minute mile?

10. Which sport did the host country, Japan, request be included in the 1964 Olympics?

11. What was originally called 'The Augusta Tournament'?

12. Which former champion jockey published his first book *Dead Cert* in 1962?

13. As of 1992, which is London's oldest Football League club?

14. What was the 'stymie' which was abolished in golf in 1951?

15. What is the weight of the men's shot-putt in official competition?

Answers on page 84

1. At what Olympic event did Harold Sakata, who played Oddjob in the film *Goldfinger*, win silver?

2. In which year was the tie-break introduced at Wimbledon?

3. Which English driver won the 1965 Indianapolis 500?

4. In which city is the Maracana Stadium?

5. Which event at the Royal International Horse Show is confined to lady riders?

6. Which country has been selected as venue for the 1998 Winter Olympic Games?

7. Where were the 1991 USA PGA Championships played?

8. In which round did Mike Tyson stop Frank Bruno in February 1989?

9. Which Irish golfer was bitten by a snake while practising for the 1992 Volvo PGA Championships at Wentworth?

10. With which American sport is Jackie Robinson associated?

11. What premier English event was won by Ballinderry Ash in 1991?

12. Who survived an emergency appendix operation, an ankle operation and being accidentally shot by his brother to go on to take professional cycling's highest honours?

13. Who won the Men's Basketball Gold Medal at the Seoul Olympics?

14. As of September 1992, who is Men's World Chess Champion?

Answers on page 84

1. Up to 1992, how many Irish golfers have won the World Match Play title since its institution in 1964?

2. Who won the 1991 Tour de France?

3. The New York Giants won the 1991 Superbowl. When had they last won the event?

4. Who were 1988 Men's Olympic Hockey Champions?

5. In which city is Randwick, Australia's oldest racecourse?

6. Who, later a successful football manager, scored all five goals for the English League against the Irish League in 1959?

7. Who became World Heavyweight boxing champion in 1937?

8. At which sport were Ireland's men World Champions in the Triples event (1984) and World Champions in the Fours event (1988)?

9. Who was 1980 Men's 1,500m Olympic Champion?

10. At what event did San Francisco 49ers' nose-tackle Michael Carter win an Olympic Silver Medal at Los Angeles in 1984?

11. Who left the Football League in 1989 to admit Maidstone United?

12. In which sport did the d'Inzeo brothers achieve international success in the 1950s and '60s?

13. Which Irishman was British Heavyweight Champion in 1972?

14. In which sport is the Thomas Cup (men) and Uber Cup (ladies) competed for internationally?

Answers on page 85

1. 'No Pride . . . No Guts . . . No Good!' To whom did this 1989 *Daily Mirror* headline refer?

2. Which queen was sketched while golfing at St Andrew's in 1563?

3. In which sport is a genoa used?

4. Which tennis player was known affectionately to fans as 'Jimbo'?

5. What is the total complement of the Oxford and Cambridge crews in the annual boat race?

6. With which sport is Robin Cousins associated?

7. Of which sport is 'sooping' an important facet?

8. Which player's transfer netted Millwall £1.5 m in March 1990?

9. Which sport do the Chicago White Sox play?

10. How many players are on a polo team?

11. Name the trophy presented to the winners of the European Football Championship.

12. In which country is Eden Gardens cricket ground?

13. What is the regulation height of a table-tennis net?

14. What have Hairy Dog, Feather Duster and Twilight Beauty in common?

15. Which tennis champion was known as the 'Ice Maiden'?

Answers on page 85

1. Who was British Champion Flat Race Jockey from 1974–77 inclusive?

2. Which country won the 1960 Olympic Hockey title foiling India's bid for a seventh successive Gold Medal?

3. Which fourteen-year-old lost to Chris Evert at Wimbledon in 1977?

4. In which Cup Final year were subs first introduced into an English Cup Final?

5. Who up to 1992 has been the youngest winner of the World Formula One Racing Driver's Championship?

6. Singer Julio Iglesias was on the books of which European soccer club?

7. In which year did Tony Jacklin win the US Open Golf Championship?

8. Why should boxer 'Bombadier' Billy Wells be familiar to cinema-goers?

9. What penalty, if any, is incurred in cricket by the use of a fielder's cap in preventing the ball from reaching the boundary?

10. Up to 1993 how many times has Bernhard Langer won the US Masters?

11. In which sport have Uhlenhorst (Germany), Bloemendaal (Netherlands) and Slough (England) all been European Club Champions?

12. Where were the 1989 World Indoor Athletic Championships held?

13. Which nation won the 1988 European Football Championship?

Answers on page 86

1. Where was the 1991 British Open Golf Championship played?

2. Who in January 1984, promised fans 'another clip around the ear 'ole' if he caught them on his pitch?

3. Which athlete took the Women's Long Jump title at the 1988 Olympics?

4. Who was England's leading Division One goalscorer (League and Cup) in the 1988–89 season?

5. Who played the lead role in the baseball film *The Natural*?

6. In which event might competitors use a scissors, free-leg swing or straddle?

7. For which English university did both Mike Gibson and John Robbie play?

8. What was the maiden name of athlete Mary Slaney?

9. Who in 1977 became the first woman chosen as *Sports Illustrated* Personality of the Year?

10. Which triple FA Cup medallist of the 1950s was known as 'Wor Jackie'?

11. About which sport was the song 'Take me out to the ballgame' written?

12. Why is the Olympic Three Day Equestrian Event a misnomer?

13. Where was the Forte PGA Seniors Golf Tournament held in 1992?

14. At which motor racing event in 1955 were eighty-two people killed?

15. What are released from a 'low-house' and a 'high-house'?

Answers on page 86

1. Which team lost 32–9 to Ireland in Brisbane in 1987?

2. Who captained the 1980 Lions on their South African tour?

3. How many of John Moloney's twenty-seven caps were at scrum-half?

4. Which Scottish player was nicknamed 'the Bear'?

5. Who scored Australia's winning try against Ireland in the 1991 World Cup?

6. Which England player was capped forty-one times between 1971 and 1980?

7. When did Ireland celebrate its Centenary Year?

8. Who captained Garryowen to their 1991–92 All-Ireland League victory?

9. With which country did J. Arigho gain sixteen international caps between 1928 and 1931?

10. Against which country did Fergus Slattery gain his last cap in 1984?

11. Name the first international touring side to play the Barbarians.

12. For which country did Gerald Bosch score twenty-two points against France in 1975?

13. Which touring team are known as 'The Eagles'?

14. Which Australian player made the error which let in Ieuan Evans for the try — and the 1989 Test series — to the Lions?

15. Who in 1900 were the first Olympic Rugby Champions?

Answers on page 87

1. Which Welsh club's home ground is Eugene Cross Park?

2. With which Leinster club did Moss Keane play his senior rugby?

3. Who in 1990 won their first Munster Senior League title?

4. What do the letters CIYMS abbreviate?

5. Which two teams compete annually for the Bowring Bowl?

6. Which Young Munster player gained fourteen international caps between 1949 and 1952?

7. In which country did seven-a-side rugby originate in 1883?

8. Who up to the 1992–93 season, with forty-five, is Ireland's most capped hooker?

9. How many caps at No. 8 did Willie Duggan gain between 1975 and 1984?

10. Who scored two tries in Ireland's 27–12 victory over Australia at Brisbane in 1979?

11. Who up to the 1992–93 season have won most Connacht Cups?

12. With which club did Willie John McBride play his senior rugby?

13. Whose was the *Captain's Diary 1989–91*?

14. Name English club Wasps' ground.

15. France now play at Parc des Princes. Where were their home internationals previously played?

Answers on page 88

1. When was the value of a try increased to four points?

2. Whom did 'Dusty' Hare displace as England's record points-scorer?

3. Which club was founded in Bradford by W.P. Carpmael in 1890?

4. Which London side's home venue is Stoop Memorial Ground?

5. Name the Mick Doyle autobiography published in 1991 by Gill and Macmillan.

6. Which Welsh club did David Watkins leave for Rugby League side Salford?

7. Against which country in 1987 did Neil Francis make his international debut?

8. Who was assistant coach to Ciaran Fitzgerald during the 1991–92 season?

9. Name the other teams in Ireland's 1991 World Cup Group.

10. Which club won the 1955 Leinster Cup with a little assistance from Cliff Morgan?

11. What is unusual about the shirt numbering system used by both Bristol and Leicester?

12. Which was the last of the four Home Unions to be formed?

13. Prior to the 1992–93 season what was the result on the last occasion (1981) when Ireland met South Africa in Dublin?

14. Who scored 113 points for Ireland between 1977 and 1988?

Answers on page 88

1. In which year did Donal Lenihan first tour with the Lions?

2. Who converted six penalties for Ireland against Scotland in 1982?

3. With which club did Colin Patterson, Ireland's scrum-half (1978–80), play?

4. How many seasons each did the international careers of both Tony O'Reilly and Mike Gibson span?

5. Which country, having lost all of its 1956–57 International Championship matches, was presented with a six-foot long wooden spoon by a disgruntled supporter?

6. Who was the Scottish captain of the 1966 Lions?

7. In which country are Rosario and San Isidoro leading clubs?

8. Who, up to the 1992–93 season, is Ireland's most capped prop?

9. Ireland first met Romania in 1980. What was the result?

10. Who captained Ireland to their 1979 Test series victory over Australia?

11. He was known to millions as 'Mike' Gibson, but what is his correct first name?

12. Who scored fifty-two points for Scotland in the 1985–86 Home International Championship?

13. Who captained the victorious Australians in the 1991 World Cup?

Answers on page 89

1. Who in 1976 was the first full-back to score two tries in an international?

2. Where in 1950 did Jack Kyle tour with the Lions?

3. Having first played England in 1875 when did Ireland record its first win?

4. Which Irish provincial side defeated the 1984 touring Australians?

5. Who led Scotland to the Triple Crown and Grand Slam in 1984?

6. Name Ulster's oldest club.

7. What was the historical significance of Tane Norton's captaincy of New Zealand against the 1977 touring Lions?

8. Who captained Ireland on their 1992 New Zealand tour?

9. Where in 1927 was the Apia Rugby Union formed?

10. In which position did Bective's George Norton win his eleven international caps?

11. With which club was Nick Popplewell playing when he gained his first international cap v New Zealand in 1989?

12. In which year and against what opposition did W.J. McBride gain his first international cap?

13. Who inflicted a 92–0 defeat on Spain in 1979?

14. Which Welsh club did Terry Cobner captain for a decade from 1969?

15. With which club did Ireland's 1949 Triple Crown-winning captain Karl Mullen, play?

Answers on page 89

1. Who scored fourteen tries for Ireland between 1920 and 1930?

2. Which full-back scored 36 points in the 1983 International Championship?

3. Who up to the 1992–93 season is Ireland's most capped full-back?

4. What had Ireland players Philip Matthews, Rob Saunders and Terry Kingston particularly in common during 1991?

5. Which England player retired after his side Leicester had lost the 1989 Cup Final, having scored 7,177 points in first-class rugby?

6. How many full International caps has Ciaran Fitzgerald?

7. Who in 1889 were England's first county champions?

8. Kevin Flynn won twenty-two international caps. With which club did he play?

9. What 'first' was achieved by Michael O'Brien on 23 April 1974?

10. Which famous 'Sevens' event has been held at Twickenham since 1926?

11. Who were the only side to inflict defeat on the Springboks during their 1960–61 tour of Great Britain and France?

12. Who captained the Lions in their 1950 tour of Australia and New Zealand?

13. Who in 1947 added an Irish Rugby Cap against Australia to his ten International Football Caps?

Answers on page 90

1. Which horse, up to 1992, was the last Irish-trained winner of the Epsom Derby?

2. How many times does the Aintree Grand National field cross the Melling Road?

3. Who won the 1992 Welsh Grand National?

4. Which major flat race was won in 1985 by Cataldi, in 1986 by K-Battery and in 1987 by Star of a Gunner?

5. Who was runner-up to Seagram in the 1991 Aintree Grand National?

6. On which course is the Anthony Mildmay, Peter Cazalet Memorial Handicap Chase run?

7. Which, if any, of the following completed the Epsom Derby/Irish Derby double: The Minstrel (1977), Shirley Heights (1978) or Troy (1979)?

8. On which horse did Willie Carson win the 1987 English 2,000 Guineas?

9. What was the starting price of the Pat Eddery-ridden 1990 Epsom Derby winner Quest for Fame?

10. Which Irish racecourse has the shortest name?

11. Who wrote *Vincent O'Brien, the Master of Ballydoyle*?

12. In which year did the now successful author Dick Francis, retire from the saddle: 1957, 1960 or 1962?

13. Which Irish jockey partnered Cool Ground to victory in the 1992 Cheltenham Gold Cup?

14. Which combination had successive Eclipse wins in 1987 and 1988?

15. Over what distance is the Tote Ebor Handicap run at York?

Answers on page 90

1. Which English rider, who died tragically in 1886 at the age of twenty-nine, was champion flat jockey on thirteen occasions?

2. Who won the fiftieth running of Cheltenham's Champion Hurdle in 1979?

3. Which winning jockey of the 1979 2,000 Guineas, became the first American in fifty-seven years to win the English Classic?

4. Of which trainer did Peter Scudamore say: 'He's a genius. It's a privilege to ride for him'?

5. Who rode Sea Pigeon to victory in the 1979 Tote Ebor Handicap?

6. After whom is Newmarket's Rowley Mile course named?

7. Which brother of Try My Best won an Irish Derby in the 1980s?

8. What was Lester Pigott's terse comment when asked to describe Monteverdi who had failed dismally in the 1980 Irish 2,000 Guineas?

9. Name Joe Mercer's father-in-law who beat him into second place in the 1959 Epsom Derby.

10. *Born Lucky* was the title of the autobiography published in 1985 of which English steeplechase jockey?

11. Where is the July Course?

12. Who succeeded Sir Gordon Richards as English Champion Jockey in 1954?

13. Name the Irish trainer of 1984 Epsom Derby winner Secreto.

Answers on page 91

1. From which stud was Shergar kidnapped on 8 February 1983?

2. What is the French equivalent of the Oaks?

3. Which jockey was used in the racing scenes of the film *The Champions*?

4. In 1984 a $1 m bonus was offered to the winner of three specific races, two in England and one in Ireland. Name the races.

5. When a racing commentator speaks of 'the distance', what does he mean?

6. Who in 1932 won the Epsom Derby on its first live TV transmission?

7. The Italian Derby is run in Rome. In which city is the Italian Oaks (Oaks d'Italia) run?

8. Who was the famous offspring of Quorum and Mared?

9. Which English trainer, incensed at the disqualification of his horse Premonition from first place in the 1953 Irish Derby, ran newsreel film of the race at his local cinema for a week?

10. Who in 1991 wrote *Horses, Lords and Racing Men*?

11. Name the winner of the 1992 Jameson Irish Grand National.

12. Which Irish course is a palindrome?

13. Who are current sponsors of the Welsh Grand National?

14. Who did Sharastani beat into second place in the 1986 Epsom Derby?

Answers on page 91

1. What is the distance of the Tote Cesarewitch at Newmarket?

2. At what odds did second-placed Brother Philips start in the 1979 Irish 2,000 Guineas won by Dickens Hill?

3. What feat has been achieved by Secretariat (1973), Seattle Slew (1977) and Affirmed (1978)?

4. In which year was the Cheltenham Gold Cup first run: 1919, 1924, 1929 or 1933?

5. On which horse did Freddie Head win his fourth Prix de l'Arc de Triomphe in 1979?

6. In 1984 a limit was placed on the number of starters for the Aintree Grand National. What number was it?

7. What did Tontine do when taking the 1825 1,000 Guineas, which no other British classic winner has since done?

8. Who in 1967 was the first Epsom Derby winner out of starting stalls?

9. Which horse finished second in the 1978 Mackeson Gold Cup, second in the 1978 Massey Ferguson Gold Cup, second in the 1979 Aintree Grand National and second in the 1979 Hennessy Gold Cup?

10. When Shirley Heights won the 1978 Epsom Derby he was repeating his sire's win in 1971. Who was that?

11. Which jockey in 1989, became the first rider to have won the English, Irish, French and Kentucky Derbies?

Answers on page 91

1. Which racecourse in Ireland, England, Scotland or Wales has the shortest name?

2. Where is the William Hill Dante Stakes run annually?

3. On which horse did Peter Scudamore win the 1988 and 1989 Welsh Grand Nationals?

4. Who sponsored the 1992 Aintree Grand National?

5. Name the English Triple Crown winner who died, aged twenty-four, on 15 April 1992 at the Claiborne Stud, Kentucky.

6. Which leading US jockey ended a 110-consecutive losing streak by winning on Father Duffy at Santa Anita on 11 February 1979?

7. Name the horse which finished second in both the Epsom and Irish Derbies of 1979.

8. What is the Irish equivalent of the French Poule d'Essai des Poulains?

9. Over what distance is the Washington DC International run?

10. Which horse won the 1966 Cheltenham Gold Cup at odds of 1/10?

11. Who headed the British Flat Race Owner's List on thirteen occasions between 1924 and 1952?

12. Who won the Epsom Derby when Glint of Gold was second and Scintillating Air third?

13. Who owned Special Cargo which won the 1984 Whitbread Gold Cup in a three-way photo?

14. Which Aintree Grand National-winning jockey announced his retirement having ridden Lumen to victory at Wetherby in 1982?

Answers on page 92

1. How many Irish racecourses begin with the letter 'D'?

2. Which two fences on the Aintree Grand National course are jumped only once?

3. Which Irishman was leading National Hunt trainer in England in 1952–53 and 1953–54 and leading flat trainer there in 1966?

4. Where is the Queen Mother Champion Chase run?

5. Which Dick Hern-trained filly won the 1980 Irish Oaks?

6. On which horse did Pat Day win the 1992 Kentucky Derby?

7. Which horse won the 1991 Jameson Irish Grand National?

8. Which 1905 Epsom Derby winner had the same name as a Roman orator-statesman and a World War II German spy's code-name?

9. In 1979 who became the first Scottish horse to win the Aintree Grand National?

10. Which Australian who rode Vaguely Noble and Levmoss to victory in the Prix de l'Arc de Triomphe, died in Melbourne in 1979?

11. On which horse did Willie Carson win his first Irish St Leger in 1979?

12. Which Irish jockey was runner-up to John Francome in the 1978–79 English National Hunt Championship?

13. With the exception of the two world wars, the Oaks has been run at Epsom since 1779. Where was it held during the war years?

Answers on page 92

1. Which World Heavyweight Champion walked out of a 1963 performance of the *Flower Drum Song* exclaiming: 'There's too much singing'?

2. By what name was Rocco Francis Marchigiano better known?

3. Which Edinburgh Lightweight took the World title from Ismael Laguna in San Jose in September 1970?

4. In which town was Muhammad Ali born on 17 January 1942?

5. Which former World Heavyweight Champion died in a car crash at the age of sixty-eight on 10 June 1946?

6. Which Olympic Games introduced compulsory headgear for all boxers?

7. In which city did John L. Sullivan lose his World title to James J. Corbett?

8. Who was Olympic Heavyweight Champion in 1964?

9. Who retired as World Heavyweight Champion having defeated Tom Heeney on 26 July 1928?

10. About which prospective opponent did Joe Louis say: 'He can run, but he can't hide'?

11. In the annals of the ring who is John Sholto Douglas universally known as?

12. Name either of the two fighters who contested the last bare-knuckle World Heavyweight Championship.

13. Which early World Heavyweight Champion was born the son of a policeman in Helston, Cornwall, England?

Answers on page 93

1. Which Heavyweight Champion, because of his stature, was known as the 'Napoleon of the ring'?

2. Who knocked Joe Louis out of the ring in the first round of their fight on 23 May 1941?

3. Up to 1992, which World Heavyweight Champion has had most professional wins inside the distance during his career?

4. Who in 1967 emerged as winner of the first computerised 'All-time Heavyweight Champion of the World'?

5. Who did Joe Frazier stop in four rounds on 16 February 1970 for the undisputed World Heavyweight title?

6. Which Heavyweight Champion was known as the 'Fighting Marine'?

7. Which World Light-Heavyweight Champion has had most wins inside the distance during his career?

8. Prior to the formation of the British Boxing Board of Control in 1918, which organisation had run the sport in Britain?

9. Who in 1930 fought for the World Heavyweight title vacated by Gene Tunney?

10. Which World Light-Heavyweight who took the title from Georges Carpentier, walked round Paris with a lion on a lead?

11. Who was World Light-Heavyweight Champion from 1952–62?

12. Who was the first grandfather to hold a World title?

Answers on page 93

1. In which year was the 'Thrilla in Manilla'?

2. Who was the first Argentinian to win a world professional title?

3. The maxim of which World Heavyweight Champion (1919 to 1926) was: 'Tall men come down to my height when I hit 'em in the body'?

4. How old was Eusebio Pedroza when losing his World Featherweight title to Barry McGuigan in 1985?

5. What historical significance had the Joe Louis v Jersey Walcott World Heavyweight Championship fight of 5 December 1947?

6. Who was 1968 Olympic Heavyweight Champion?

7. In which year did Charlie Nash take the European Lightweight title from Frenchman Andre Holyk?

8. Who was British Heavyweight Champion from 1959–69?

9. In what round did Mike Tyson KO Michael Spinks in Atlantic City on 28 June 1988?

10. Who became Undisputed World Light-Heavyweight Champion in 1988?

11. Where did Jess Williard take the World Heavyweight title from Jack Johnson on 5 April 1915?

12. The first names of which colourful fighter were Maxmillian Adalbert?

13. How is the name of a titled Englishman, Hugh Lowther, perpetuated in the annals of the ring?

14. Who was the first German to hold a World Boxing title?

Answers on page 94

1. From whom did Freddie Mills take the World Light-Heavyweight title in 1948?

2. Who was 'the ghost with a hammer in his hand'?

3. Which Canadian regained the World Light-Heavyweight title on 26 June 1988?

4. What is the maximum weight for a Middleweight?

5. How many world titles did Thomas Hearns win at different weights?

6. Which Clare-born boxer was World Light-Heavyweight Champion from 1923–25?

7. Who up to 1992 has been the tallest World Heavyweight Champion?

8. Who became World Heavyweight Champion on 25 September 1962 by a one-round knockout of Floyd Patterson?

9. Who, in only his eighth professional fight defeated Muhammad Ali for the World title on 18 February 1978?

10. Which Heavyweight Champion was nicknamed the 'Black Uhlan'?

11. Who were the first brothers to fight (at different times) for the World Heavyweight Championship?

12. Which Middleweight twice beat Sugar Ray Robinson in title fights before successfully defending the crown against Terry Downes?

13. Under what name did Cuban Gerado Gonzales hold the World Welterweight title from 1950–54?

Answers on page 94

1. Who, on losing his World Heavyweight title in 1937 said: 'When he knocked me down I could have stayed there for three weeks'?

2. Who, on a controversial points decision took Henry Cooper's European Heavyweight title in March 1971?

3. Who was 1960 Olympic Light-Heavyweight Champion?

4. World Middleweight Champion (1940–48), he was nicknamed 'Man of Steel'. Who was he?

5. At which weight was Jake La Motta World Champion from 1949–51?

6. In which city did Ingemar Johansson win and lose his world title?

7. At which weight did Emile Griffith win, lose, regain and vacate a world title?

8. At which weight did Chris Finnegan win an Olympic Gold Medal in 1968?

9. In which country was 1981 World Featherweight and Super-Featherweight Champion, Azumah Nelson born?

10. Which dual World Champion was born Barnet Rosofsky in New York on 23 December 1909?

11. Which Hungarian triple Olympic Champion became European Middleweight Champion in 1962?

12. At what weight did Alan Rudkin hold European and Commonwealth titles?

13. Which brothers won Olympic Gold Medals at Montreal in 1976?

Answers on page 95

1. Who took the 1991 All-Ireland Under-21 title?

2. Name two of the four players sent to the line in the 1983 Senior All-Ireland Final.

3. Name the Liam Hayes book dealing with Meath's great run of success.

4. Which was the first county to achieve four consecutive Senior All-Ireland victories?

5. Which Mayo player received a 1982 Bank of Ireland All-Time All-Star award?

6. With which Ulster county did P.J. Duke win an All-Ireland Senior medal?

7. In which year did the attendance at an All-Ireland Final first top 50,000?

8. Who was the first Armagh man to become President of the GAA?

9. Whom did Kerry defeat to take the Centenary League Championship?

10. Which province took the first Railway Cup in 1927?

11. What are the county colours of Fermanagh?

12. Where was the Centenary GAA Congress held?

13. Kerry defeated Cork in three successive Munster Finals from 1912–14. What was Cork's score on each occasion?

14. Which county recorded four successive Connacht Senior title wins from 1977–80?

15. Who did Meath defeat in the 1991 Leinster Senior Football Final?

Answers on page 95

1. Which Kerry writer wrote the ballad 'Who can beat the Kingdom Sweet'?

2. The 1979 GAA President, Paddy McFlynn, is a native of which county?

3. Which county took its eighth All-Ireland Minor title in 1991?

4. Which province won the Centenary Railway Cup?

5. Whose second-half penalty did Paddy Cullen save in the 1977 All-Ireland Final against Armagh?

6. From which county were Walterstown, defeated 2–10 to 0–5 by Nemo Rangers (Cork) in the Centenary Club Championship?

7. Who scored Cork's last-minute goal in 1983 which foiled Kerry's bid for five successive All-Irelands?

8. Who took the first Leinster Senior Championship in 1888?

9. Which province foiled Ulster's five-in-a-row Railway Cup attempt when winning 1–9 to 0–11 in 1967?

10. At which All-Ireland Final were two national anthems played?

11. Who captained Dublin to the Sam Maguire in 1976 and 1977?

12. With which county did Tom 'Gega' O'Connor play in the 1940s?

13. Which Armagh referee handled the 1979 Kerry-Dublin All-Ireland Senior Final?

Answers on page 96

1. With which club did Kerry's Mike Sheehy play?

2. For what off-the-field occurrence did Dublin captain and team manager Tony Hanahoe receive a one-month suspension in 1978?

3. Name the Kerry player sent to the line in the 1979 Senior All-Ireland Final.

4. Who were the first team in the 1900s to retain the All-Ireland Senior Championship?

5. Who won the All-Ireland 1992 Club Championship?

6. Who in 1937 were the first Ulster county to take the All-Ireland Minor Championship?

7. Name the first Leinster player to captain successive Sam Maguire winning teams.

8. As a seventeen-year-old he played for Kerry in an All-Ireland Senior Final. His 1914 book *How to Play Gaelic Football* was the code's first manual of instruction. Name him.

9. In which year was the value of a goal reduced from five points to three?

10. Who led Down to their 1991 All-Ireland Senior success?

11. Which province recorded six goals and seven points in taking the 1975 Railway Cup?

12. Which Dublin player of the 1970s was nicknamed the 'blue panther'?

13. As of 1992, which county leads the All-Ireland Under-21 list with eight titles?

14. Who scored 2–9 for losing All-Ireland semi-finalists Offaly v Kerry in 1980?

Answers on page 96

1. Who in 1979 became the first Listowel player to lead Kerry to an All-Ireland Senior title?

2. Which manager charted Offaly's 1982 All-Ireland Senior success?

3. As of 1991 how many All-Ireland Senior titles have Dublin won?

4. Who in 1929 were crowned first All-Ireland Minor Football Champions?

5. Which county recorded six successive Ulster Senior titles from 1908–13?

6. Which Galway player had a second-half penalty saved by Paddy Cullen in the 1974 All-Ireland Final?

7. From which GAA President did Tony Hanahoe receive the Sam Maguire in 1978?

8. Which columnist described the second half of the 1977 Dublin-Kerry Semi-Final encounter as 'The greatest thirty minutes of football since the days you could buy a pint for ninepence'?

9. Who was Brian Mullins' regular midfield partner from 1975–79?

10. For which county did Tom McCreesh and Paddy Moriarty appear in a 1970s All-Ireland Senior Final?

11. Whom did Kerry defeat in the replayed National Football League Final at Croke Park on 26 May 1974?

12. Which Dublin player courteously handed Mike Sheehy the ball which the Kerry player promptly lobbed over Paddy Cullen into the net in the 1978 All-Ireland Final?

Answers on page 97

1. P.D. Mehigan was known as 'Carberry' to many. Under what pen-name did he write for *The Irish Times*?

2. Wexford, successful 1915 All-Ireland Senior Champions, were trained by the man who fought Tommy Burns for the World Heavyweight Boxing Championship in Dublin in 1908. Who was he?

3. Which Kerry defender failed to gather the ball which Offaly's Seamus Darby crashed into the net for the winning score in the 1982 All-Ireland Final?

4. In which city did Kerry 'lose' the Sam Maguire in 1981?

5. Who wrote *The Who's Who of Gaelic Games*?

6. Which player did Offaly fly back from the USA to play in the 1982 All-Ireland Final?

7. Name Down's captain in their 1968 All-Ireland Final win over Kerry.

8. Which two teams in 1953 attracted the first attendance in excess of 80,000 at an All-Ireland Football Final?

9. Who was the youngest player on Ireland's 1986 Australian Tour?

10. On which team did Kerry inflict a two-point defeat in the 1991 Munster Senior Football Final?

11. Which Dublin player received the 1976 and 1977 Texaco Footballer of the Year award?

12. Who refereed the 1978 Dublin-Kerry All-Ireland Senior Final?

13. Which Cavan player captained Ulster to 1942 and '43 Railway Cup victories?

Answers on page 97

1. Which Kerry player of the 1970s and 1980s graduated as a physical education teacher at Loughborough College in England?

2. Who captained Dublin to their 1974 Sam Maguire victory over Galway?

3. Who were defeated 0–10 to 0–8 by Meath in the Centenary Cup Final?

4. Who in 1985 succeeded Paddy Buggy as GAA President?

5. Name either of the players sent to the line in the 1978 All-Ireland Senior Final.

6. Who scored 3–2 in the 1978 All-Ireland Senior Football Final?

7. Who captained Dublin to their 1991 National League title?

8. Which county won its twenty-first Senior All-Ireland title in 1983?

9. Who in 1974 were inaugural winners of the Ladies All-Ireland Senior Football Championship?

10. Name the GAA's Press and Public Relations Officer.

11. Who captained Meath in their 1987 All-Ireland win over Cork?

12. Who was Texaco Footballer of the Year in both 1984 and 1985?

13. Which Roscommon team lost the 1987 and 1988 All-Ireland Club Championships?

14. Who are official sponsors of the National Football League?

Answers on page 98

1. Which team did Dan O'Neill captain to All-Ireland success in 1991?

2. Name Limerick's outstanding goalkeeper who played in five All-Ireland Senior Finals between 1933 and 1940.

3. Who in 1981 was Offaly's first Texaco Hurler of the Year?

4. Which sponsor's name appeared on the Clare jerseys in their 1992 Munster Championship meetings with Waterford?

5. Up to 1992, when had Kerry last won an All-Ireland Senior Hurling title?

6. Who, coming on as substitute, scored a vital Galway goal in the 1988 All-Ireland Final against Tipperary?

7. In which village was Christy Ring born in 1920?

8. When did Waterford win its first Munster Senior Hurling title?

9. How many Senior All-Irelands did Kilkenny win in the 1950s?

10. *A Lifetime in Hurling* (1955) is the story of which Tipperary hurler?

11. Which county were Leinster Minor Hurling Champions between 1971 and 1979?

12. Who captained losing All-Ireland finalists Offaly in the Centenary Final at Thurles?

13. Who won the Royal Liver National League in its inaugural year?

14. Name the Dublin goalkeeper who played in Leinster's 1953 and '54 Railway Cup teams.

Answers on page 98

1. With which counties did 'Drug' Walsh and 'Bowler' Walsh play?

2. Who scored the only goal in the 1991 All-Ireland Senior Hurling Final?

3. Who in 1983 were the first team to carry the All-Ireland Club Hurling title across the border?

4. Up to 1992 how many Senior All-Ireland titles has Laois won?

5. Name Kilkenny's captain in their 1988 All-Ireland Senior Camogie win over Cork.

6. Who captained Wexford to the 1968 Liam McCarthy Cup?

7. Which team won the inaugural All-Ireland Club Championship in 1971?

8. The winners of what competition receive the Thomas Ashe Cup?

9. Who won the All-Ireland Senior Colleges Championship in the first four years of the competition?

10. Which Kilkenny player recorded fourteen points in the 1963 All-Ireland Senior Hurling Final?

11. Which teams attracted a 77,854 attendance at the 1955 All-Ireland Final?

12. When did Christy Ring captain Cork to successive All-Ireland Senior Championships?

13. Which county leads the Camogie Senior All-Ireland Roll of Honour with twenty-six wins up to 1992?

14. Near which town is the annual Poc Fada event staged?

Answers on page 98

1. In which year did Limerick win its first under-21 title?

2. Which Limerick hurler represented his county and province in both codes and was a provincial and All-Ireland medal winner in the shot, discus and hammer?

3. Name the author of the 727-page *Tipperary's GAA Story*.

4. What have the following Corkmen in common: Derry Beckett, Denis Coughlan and Brian Murphy?

5. Who were the defeated semi-finalists in the Centenary All-Ireland?

6. Phelim Murphy and Bernie O'Connor were for many years associated with teams from which county?

7. He captained Tipperary to All-Ireland Senior Hurling victories in 1906 and 1908. How is his name perpetuated in his native county?

8. Who did London defeat to win the 1901 All-Ireland Senior title?

9. Up to 1992 Clare has but one All-Ireland Senior title to its credit. When was this achieved?

10. How many times did Jimmy Doyle captain Tipperary to the Liam McCarthy Cup?

11. In which year did Galway win its first Minor All-Ireland title?

12. Who scored ten points for Limerick in their 1973 All-Ireland Senior Hurling success against Kilkenny?

13. Name the Leinster-man who captained Munster to 1981 Railway Cup victory over Leinster.

14. By whom were Laois defeated in their last appearance (up to 1992) in an All-Ireland Senior Final?

Answers on page 99

1. Which GAA congress fixed the first Sunday in September as All-Ireland Hurling Final day?

2. Which Laois referee handled the 1978 Kilkenny/Cork All-Ireland Senior Final?

3. The winners of what camogie competition receive the Ashbourne Cup?

4. Which, up to 1992, was the only year in which Kilkenny failed to register a score in a Leinster Senior Hurling Final?

5. 'And while the Gaels may congregate, To watch men play with stick and ball, I thank the Lord that I have lived, To see the greatest of them all.' Whose death on 13 September 1982, provoked this tribute in the *Tipperary Star*?

6. In which Leinster town is O'Moore Park a popular venue?

7. Which county achieved a hat-trick of Oireachtas wins in the period 1978–80?

8. Name the Antrim goalkeeper who captained Loughgiel Shamrocks in the 1983 All-Ireland Club Championship.

9. Who was selected as Bank of Ireland All-Star goalkeeper from 1972–76?

10. Which team captained by Bob McConkey, won the Liam McCarthy Cup in the first year it was put up for competition?

11. Who was the only Cork player chosen on the 1987 Bank of Ireland All-Stars team?

Answers on page 99

1. Which Leinster referee handled the 1988 Galway v Tipperary All-Ireland Senior Final?

2. Who were the first Connacht team to win the All-Ireland Club Championship?

3. Which teams needed two replays to decide the 1966 All-Ireland Under-21 title?

4. Who was Noel Skehan's immediate predecessor as Kilkenny goalkeeper?

5. How many Senior All-Irelands did Galway win in the 1980s?

6. Who was Bank of Ireland All-Star goalkeeper in 1977, '78 and '81?

7. Name the trophy presented to the All-Ireland Club Hurling Champions.

8. Which Kerry-born playwright and novelist wrote 'A Song for Christy Ring'?

9. Who was the first man to captain three Senior All-Ireland winning teams?

10. With which club did the Rackard brothers of Wexford play?

11. Who captained Cork to the inaugural League Championship in 1926?

12. Which former Clare star has six Railway Cup medals?

13. Who are the main beneficiaries of the Oireachtas competition?

14. How many Senior All-Ireland Hurling medals has former Taoiseach Jack Lynch won?

15. Who captained Kilkenny to their 1974 Senior All-Ireland Championship success?

Answers on page 100

Answers

Golf (I)

1. The US Masters.
2. Eight.
3. William.
4. John O'Leary.
5. Ten.
6. Arnold Palmer.
7. Miss Clarrie Tiernan.
8. £100.
9. South Carolina.
10. Royal Troon (the eighth hole).
11. Joint second (with Brian Huggett) to Peter Thomson in 1965.
12. At Augusta National (home of the US Masters).
13. Bobby Locke (South Africa).
14. Turnberry.
15. Isao Aoki (Hawaiian Open).

Golf (II)

1. Severiano Ballesteros.
2. Nick Faldo (1983).
3. Tony Jacklin.
4. Bob Tway.
5. Australia.
6. Fred Couples.
7. The World Matchplay Championship.
8. Ben Hogan.
9. 1980.
10. 1986: Jack Nicklaus (Masters) at forty-six years of age and Raymond Floyd at forty-three years of age.
11. David Graham.
12. The eleventh, twelfth and thirteenth.
13. Ben Hogan.
14. Three (1953, 1958 and 1960).

15. Eighteen: Six US Masters, five US PGAs, four US
    Opens and three British Opens. (He also won two US
    Amateur titles.)

Golf (III)

1. 1980.
2. Isao Aoki.
3. Philomena Garvey (she was also runner-up on three
   occasions).
4. Twenty-two years of age.
5. Jack Nicklaus.
6. The Oxford and Cambridge Golfing Society.
7. 1938.
8. Scott Hoch.
9. Mexico City.
10. Turnberry, 1986.
11. £40,000.
12. False: the Walker Cup (1922) is five years older.
13. Killarney.
14. The Harry Vardon Trophy.
15. Christy O'Connor Snr (with £31,532).

Golf (IV)

1. 1957 (at Lindrick).
2. Peru (it is the world's highest course).
3. Severiano Ballesteros.
4. Sandy Lyle.
5. Royal County Down.
6. Ninety-two (and halved twelve).
7. Jack Nicklaus (at the 5th).
8. Sony.
9. Arnold Palmer (USA).
10. Severiano Ballesteros.
11. Ronan Rafferty.
12. Argentina.
13. Bernhard Langer.

Golf (V)

1. Bruce Crampton.
2. The winner of the British Open. (It is an affectionate name for the trophy.)
3. Royal St George.
4. Portmarnock.
5. Gary Player.
6. Bernhard Langer (by ten shots).
7. 1955.
8. Fred Daly.
9. Royal Birkdale.
10. Mr Lu.
11. The British Amateur Championship (first played 20–23 April 1885).
12. Lillian Behan, Claire Hourihane and Mary McKenna.
13. Roberto de Vicenzo.
14. Jack Nicklaus.

Golf (VI)

1. Fuzzy Zoeller.
2. Gary Player.
3. Ian Woosnam.
4. 1985.
5. Hubert Green.
6. Greg Norman.
7. 1955.
8. Bobby Locke.
9. Because of a petrol shortage caused by the Suez crisis.
10. The player from Great Britain and Ireland who achieves the lowest round in the British Open Championship.
11. James Bruen.
12. Jose Maria Olazabal.
13. Troon.

Golf (VII)

1. Ken Brown.
2. Nick Price.
3. The youngest winner of the title at seventeen years, 249 days.
4. Greg Norman.
5. Tony Jacklin.
6. Christy O'Connor Snr.
7. Severiano Ballesteros.
8. Mary McKenna.
9. Ten.
10. Hoylake.
11. Portmarnock.
12. Severiano Ballesteros and Greg Norman.

Darts

1. Keith Deller.
2. 17:15 treble 20s, treble 17 and Bull.
3. Leighton Rees.
4. Finland.
5. 1980.
6. Wales.
7. Leighton Rees (by John Lowe).
8. Stefan Lord (Sweden).
9. Jocky Wilson.
10. John Lowe (who earned £102,000 for the feat).
11. 4 and 9.
12. Eric Bristow's.
13. John Lowe.

Snooker (I)

1. India.
2. Stephen Hendry.
3. Patsy Fagan.
4. Steve Davis (who defeated John Parrott).

5. Walter Donaldson.
6. Jimmy White.
7. Ken Doherty.
8. Steve Davis (1982–84).
9. Three.
10. Terry Griffiths.
11. Steve Davis (1984).
12. 1928 (by Joe Davis).
13. The Dulux British Open (won by Silvino Francisco).
14. Edinburgh.
15. Doug Mountjoy.

Snooker (II)

1. Dennis Taylor.
2. Manchester (Wythenshaw Forum).
3. Fred Davis.
4. Wembley Conference Centre.
5. Tony Knowles.
6. Steve Davis achieved the first televised maximum break (147) during the competition.
7. Kirk Stevens.
8. £105,000.
9. Joe Davis.
10. Alex Higgins.
11. Cliff Thorburn.
12. One (Alex Higgins).
13. The second televised maximum break (147).

Snooker (III)

1. Three feet.
2. South African.
3. 1983.
4. They are left-handed.
5. Six.
6. London.

7. Ray Reardon (49 years).
8. Steve Davis and Dennis Taylor (winner) in the final of the Embassy World Championship.
9. Steve Davis.
10. Steve Davis (winner) and Joe Johnson.
11. Terry Griffiths (by 24–16).
12. Tony Meo.
13. Stephen Hendry.
14. Ireland's Stephen O'Connor.
15. 1891.

Soccer (I)

1. The Belgian League.
2. Bert Trautmann (Manchester City).
3. 1950 (Arsenal won 2–0).
4. By winning the competition the previous season.
5. Real Madrid.
6. George Best.
7. Tom Finney (Preston and England).
8. Perth.
9. Mexico.
10. Jack Charlton.
11. The winners of the South American Club Championship.
12. 105 times.
13. Lee Sharp (Manchester United).
14. Frank Stapleton's.
15. Sir Stanley Rous.

Soccer (II)

1. Berwick Rangers.
2. Packie Bonner.
3. One (Preston North End).
4. Noel Cantwell (Coventry City).
5. Aston Villa.

6. Arsenal.
7. 'Spot the Ball'. (The first prize in 1928 was £500.)
8. Burnden Park, Bolton.
9. Hidegkuti.
10. Jimmy Hill.
11. Martin Peters.
12. Dave Sexton.
13. Bournemouth.

Soccer (III)

1. Peter Shilton.
2. David Kelly.
3. Portsmouth are nicknamed 'Pompey'. (Pompeii was the city buried by an eruption of Vesuvius.)
4. Alfredo di Stefano.
5. Glentoran by Waterford.
6. Trevor Francis.
7. 6 February 1958.
8. (Littlewoods) Football Pools.
9. Hampden Park.
10. Spain (4–3 in 1929).
11. Stanley Matthews.
12. Ron Yeats.
13. Brazil (winners by 4–1) and Italy.
14. Tommy Docherty.
15. Joe Fagan.

Soccer (IV)

1. George Best.
2. Sunderland, Everton, Luton and Port Vale.
3. Nat Lofthouse.
4. All have managed Brazil during these periods.
5. Rotherham United.
6. The Players' Union, later to become the Professional Footballers' Association.

7. The offside law was amended from three defenders between attacker and goal to two.
8. Grimsby Town.
9. Frank O'Farrell.
10. Huddersfield Town.
11. Notts County.
12. It was the day on which the USA knocked England out of the World Cup by 1–0.
13. Bristol Rovers (Payne was a last-minute replacement on the side).

Soccer (V)

1. Aston Villa (beat Bayern Munich 1–0).
2. Manchester City.
3. Jimmy Hill.
4. Diego Maradona (by Barcelona from Boca Juniors and Argentinos Juniors).
5. Wales (it was England's first defeat on Welsh soil).
6. West Ham (Brooking) and Glasgow Celtic.
7. Clyde.
8. Gary Lineker.
9. Norwich City.
10. Derby County (beating Charlton 4–1).
11. Norwich City (2–1).
12. Portadown.
13. Glasgow Celtic.
14. Mark Lawrenson.
15. Lord Justice Taylor.

Soccer (VI)

1. Poznan.
2. Bayern Munich.
3. Five.
4. Wimbledon.
5. Ronnie Moran.
6. Manchester United.

7. Sheedy, Houghton, Townsend, Cascarino and O'Leary.
8. *You'll Never Walk Alone*.
9. Paddy Mulligan.
10. Bill Shankly.
11. Turkey (17 October 1990).
12. Sweden.
13. Ipswich Town.

Soccer (VII)

1. Tottenham Hotspur.
2. Arsenal v Cardiff City in 1927.
3. Chelsea.
4. John Charles.
5. J. Greaves (3), R. Smith (2) and D. Mackay (1) for Scotland.
6. Bob Stokoe.
7. Aberdeen.
8. Breitner.
9. France.
10. Sampdoria.
11. Middlesbrough.
12. Glasgow Celtic.
13. Cork City.

Soccer (VIII)

1. David Kelly (v Israel, 10 November 1987).
2. *Green Gunners*.
3. Gordon Strachan (Leeds United).
4. Sixteen.
5. Tommy Docherty.
6. Don Revie.
7. The League Cup.
8. Czechoslovakia (beat West Germany).
9. Arsenal, Everton, Manchester United and Newcastle United.
10. Sam Allardyce.

11. Bryon Butler.
12. Real Madrid.
13. Fifty.

Soccer (IX)

1. Racing Club (Argentina).
2. Ron Atkinson.
3. Viv Anderson (v Czechoslovakia).
4. Bobby Charlton.
5. Clydebank.
6. Old Trafford (Chelsea won 2–1 in extra time).
7. France.
8. 8–0.
9. Glasgow Celtic (beat Dundee United 2–1).
10. Ipswich Town.
11. Dundee United.
12. Newcastle United.
13. Arsenal and Tottenham Hotspur.
14. 1967 (Shamrock Rovers, winners, v St Patrick's Athletic).

Soccer (X)

1. Liam Brady (Ireland v Bulgaria 1987).
2. Gordon Banks and Pat Jennings.
3. Mick Byrne.
4. Everton and Leeds United.
5. £5.5 m.
6. George Graham (Arsenal).
7. George Best.
8. Thirteen.
9. USA (beat Norway 2–1).
10. Belgium.
11. Ricardo Villa.
12. 1981 (29 September).
13. Steve McMahon.
14. Bristol City ('Robins') and Bristol Rovers.

American Football

1. One.
2. Los Angeles.
3. To the Giants Stadium.
4. Twenty-six.
5. Seattle.
6. Dallas ('Cowboys') and Kansas City.
7. Eleven.
8. Yardage.
9. Philadelphia.
10. Left tackle.
11. Denver.
12. Huddle.
13. New England Patriots.
14. Six. (There are additional officials off-field monitoring the 'instant' TV play-backs.)
15. New York Giants.

Motor Racing

1. Alfa Romeo.
2. Emerson Fittipaldi, who was 25 years and 273 days when he took the 1972 title.
3. South African.
4. 'Keke' Rosberg.
5. Ferrari.
6. Thirty-nine.
7. McLaren.
8. Australia.
9. Niki Lauda.
10. James Hunt.
11. Brabham-Ford.
12. Four: 1955–58 inclusive.
13. Enzo Ferrari.

Equestrianism

1. Ireland.
2. Punchestown.
3. Ian Stark.
4. Buttevant Boy.
5. Seamus Hayes.
6. Gucci.
7. Hugo Simon.
8. Eddie Macken (to Germany's Hartwig Steenken).
9. Noel C. Duggan.
10. Dressage.
11. Paul Darragh (on Pele).
12. Kerrygold.
13. 1979.
14. Stockholm in 1912.
15. Goodbye III.

Tennis (I)

1. Jimmy Connors (on grass, Forest Hills '74; clay, Forest Hills '76; cement, Flushing Meadow '78, '82 and '83).
2. Ivan Lendl's.
3. Chris Lewis (New Zealand).
4. Martina Navratilova.
5. Three (1974, '76 and '81).
6. Maureen Connolly (USA).
7. Czechoslovakia.
8. Ivan Lendl.
9. Czechoslovakia.
10. Virginia Wade.
11. Germany.
12. A mouse on Court One and a sparrow on the Centre Court.
13. Pat Cash (Australia).
14. Mats Wilander.
15. USA.

Tennis (II)

1. Jim Courier (USA).
2. Steffi Graf.
3. Bjorn Borg.
4. Don Budge (USA).
5. Andrea Jaeger.
6. Andre Agassi (USA).
7. Fitzgerald, Australia; Jarryd, Sweden.
8. Charlton Heston. (McEnroe's comment was: 'That's all right, people walk out of his movies too.')
9. Suzanne Lenglen (France), who took the Singles, Ladies Doubles and Mixed Doubles.
10. Boris Becker.
11. Bjorn Borg.
12. Martina Navratilova.
13. 1877.

Cycling

1. 1982.
2. Bernard Hinault.
3. 1927 (won by A. Binda of Italy).
4. (West) Germany.
5. Sean Yates.
6. Etienne de Wilde (Belgium).
7. Eddy Merckx.
8. Amateur.
9. 1988, when A. Kirchenko won the Seoul event.
10. It was the drug to which winner Pedro Delgado twice tested positively. The result stood, the substance not being on the banned list of the International Cycling Union.
11. Laurent Fignon (France).
12. The Tour de l'Avenir.
13. None.
14. Pedro Delgado.
15. 1903.

Athletics (I)

1. Villanova.
2. Rosa Mota (Portugal).
3. Stockholm, 1912.
4. Tokyo.
5. The Pentathlon.
6. It is lit by the sun's rays.
7. Four: 1962, '67, '69 and '72.
8. Abebe Bikila (Ethiopia).
9. Rome, 1960.
10. Sergei Bubka (Ukraine).
11. 1954 (in a time of 3:59.4).
12. Pietro Mennea (Italy).
13. John Lenihan (Kerry).
14. Greek (Spiridon Louis, an eighteen-year-old shepherd).

Athletics (II)

1. Peter Snell (New Zealand).
2. Berlin, 1936.
3. John Walker (New Zealand) in 1975.
4. Mike Powell (USA) — 29' 4.5" (8:95 m).
5. Dublin (in a time of 3:54.5)
6. John Griffin.
7. USA (in world record time of 0:37.50).
8. Rosses Point, Co. Sligo.
9. Joan Benoit (USA).
10. Avery Brundage.
11. USA.
12. Lynn Jennings (USA).
13. Burt Lancaster.

Athletics (III)

1. Eamon Coghlan, Marcus O'Sullivan, Ray Flynn, Frank

O'Mara (Coghlan's name appears three times on the list).
2. The USSR (as it then was).
3. Niall Bruton.
4. CDL Coalite.
5. The first four.
6. Maricka Puica (Romania).
7. Ten.
8. Ralph Boston (USA, 1960).
9. Herb Elliott (Australia).
10. Hungary.
11. Oslo.
12. Thirty-five (twenty-eight hurdles and seven water jumps).
13. Daley Thompson.

Athletics (IV)

1. Lasse Viren (Finland).
2. Telstar, the then new communications system.
3. John Carlos and Tommie Smith.
4. Buster Crabbe.
5. Eamon Coghlan's.
6. Liz McColgan (GB).
7. Sonia O'Sullivan.
8. Mosney, Co. Meath.
9. Roger Kingdom.
10. Chris Brasher.
11. Tessa Sanderson.
12. Ann Packer (800 m, Tokyo 1964).

Athletics (V)

1. The USSR.
2. Brian Hooper.
3. Japan (Hiromi Taniguchi).

4. John Buckley (Cork).
5. Frank O'Mara.
6. Peter Snell.
7. Katrin Krabbe (Germany).
8. Jesse Owens.
9. London 1908. (Previously the winner received silver and the runner-up bronze. No award was given for third place.)
10. Dwight Stones (USA).
11. The New York Marathon.
12. As a result of the introduction of the fibreglass pole.
13. Los Angeles (1932).

A Sporting Mix (I)

1. US athlete Carl Lewis.
2. John Ngugi (Kenya).
3. The shuffle or dance executed by Cincinnati player Ickey Woods before Superbowl XXIII.
4. Austria.
5. Australian Rules Football.
6. Said Aouita (Morocco).
7. Nottingham Forest.
8. 1981.
9. Herb Elliott (Australia).
10. Judo.
11. The US Masters at Augusta National golf course.
12. Dick Francis.
13. Fulham (formed 1879, turned professional 1898).
14. When a ball blocked an opponent's line to the hole.
15. 16 lbs (7.25 kg).

A Sporting Mix (II)

1. Weight-lifting.
2. 1971.

3. Jim Clark.
4. Rio de Janeiro.
5. The Queen Elizabeth II Cup.
6. Japan.
7. Crooked Stick.
8. Round Five.
9. David Feherty.
10. Baseball (first coloured player to play in Major League).
11. The Greyhound Derby.
12. Greg Le Mond.
13. The USSR (as it then was).
14. Gary Kasparov.

A Sporting Mix (III)

1. None.
2. Miguel Induran (Spain).
3. 1987.
4. Great Britain.
5. Sydney (established 1833).
6. Brian Clough.
7. Joe Louis.
8. Bowls.
9. Sebastian Coe.
10. The Shot Putt.
11. Darlington.
12. Showjumping.
13. Danny McAlinden.
14. Badminton.

A Sporting Mix (IV)

1. England's cricket squad who had been humiliated in the Test series by the visiting Australians.
2. Mary, Queen of Scots.

3. Sailing (it is a large jib).
4. Jimmy Connors.
5. Eighteen (eight oarsmen and a cox in each crew).
6. Ice-skating.
7. Curling (it is the art of using the broom ahead of the curling stone to obtain maximum distance).
8. Tony Cascarino (to Aston Villa).
9. Baseball.
10. Four.
11. The Henry Delauney Trophy.
12. India (Calcutta).
13. Six inches.
14. All are artificial flies used in angling.
15. Chris Evert.

A Sporting Mix (V)

1. Pat Eddery.
2. Pakistan.
3. Tracy Austin.
4. 1967 (Chelsea v Spurs).
5. Emmerson Fittipaldi (Brazil), 25 years, 273 days when he took the 1972 title.
6. Real Madrid.
7. 1970.
8. He is the man who beats the massive gong which introduces Rank Organisation films.
9. The batting side is awarded five runs.
10. Once (1985).
11. Hockey.
12. Budapest.
13. Holland.

A Sporting Mix (VI)

1. Royal Birkdale.

2. Brian Clough, manager of Nottingham Forest Football Club.
3. Jackie Joyner-Kersee (USA).
4. John Aldridge (Liverpool).
5. Robert Redford.
6. The High Jump.
7. Cambridge.
8. (Mary) Decker.
9. Chris Evert.
10. Jackie Milburn (Newcastle United).
11. Baseball.
12. It is held over four days (the dressage occupies the first two).
13. Royal Dublin.
14. The Le Mans 24-hour Race.
15. Clay pigeons.

Rugby Union (I)

1. Tonga.
2. Bill Beaumont.
3. Twenty-three (the remainder were on the wing).
4. Iain Milne.
5. Michael Lynagh.
6. Tony Neary.
7. 1974–75.
8. Philip Danaher.
9. Ireland.
10. France.
11. Australia in 1948 (Barbarians won 9–6).
12. South Africa.
13. The USA.
14. David Campese.
15. France.

Rugby Union (II)

1. Ebbw Vale.
2. Lansdowne.
3. Highfield.
4. Church of Ireland Young Men's Society.
5. Oxford and Cambridge.
6. Tom Clifford.
7. Scotland (as a fund-raising idea of Melrose butcher Ned Haig).
8. Ken Kennedy (Queens University and London Irish).
9. Thirty-nine.
10. Colin Patterson.
11. UCG.
12. Ballymena.
13. England's Will Carling.
14. Sudbury.
15. Stade Colombes.

Rugby Union (III)

1. During the 1971–72 season.
2. Bob Hiller.
3. Barbarians.
4. Harlequins.
5. *Doyler*.
6. Newport.
7. Tonga.
8. John Moloney.
9. Scotland, Japan and Zimbabwe.
10. Bective Rangers.
11. Letters rather than numbers are used.
12. Wales in 1880.
13. South Africa won 12–10.
14. Tony Ward.

Rugby Union (IV)

1. 1983 (New Zealand).
2. Ollie Campbell.
3. Instonians.
4. Sixteen.
5. France.
6. Mike Campbell-Lamerton.
7. Argentina.
8. Phil Orr (58).
9. A 13-all draw.
10. Fergus Slattery.
11. Cameron.
12. Gavin Hastings.
13. Nick Farr-Jones.

Rugby Union (V)

1. J.P.R. Williams (v England).
2. New Zealand.
3. 1887.
4. Ulster.
5. Jim Aitken.
6. Queens University, founded 1868.
7. He was the first Maori to captain the All-Blacks.
8. Philip Danaher.
9. Western Samoa.
10. Full-back.
11. Greystones.
12. 1962 against England at Twickenham (Ireland lost 16–0).
13. France.
14. Pontypool.
15. Old Belvedere.

Rugby Union (VI)

1. George Stephenson.
2. Serge Blanco.
3. Tom Kiernan (UCC and Cork Constitution) with fifty-four caps (1960–73).
4. Each of them captained Ireland.
5. 'Dusty' Hare.
6. Twenty-five.
7. Yorkshire.
8. Wanderers.
9. He was Twickenham's first streaker (he was later fined £10).
10. The Middlesex Sevens.
11. The Barbarians, 6–0 in Cardiff.
12. Karl Mullen.
13. (Dr) Kevin O'Flanagan.

Racing (I)

1. Secreto (1984).
2. Twice.
3. Carvill's Hill (Peter Scudamore).
4. The William Hill Lincoln.
5. Garrison Savannah.
6. Sandown.
7. All three.
8. Don't Forget Me.
9. 7–1.
10. Naas.
11. Raymond Smith.
12. 1957.
13. Adrian Maguire.
14. Mtoto ridden by Michael Roberts.
15. One mile, six furlongs.

Racing (II)

1. Fred Archer.
2. Monksfield (D.T. Hughes).
3. Steve Cauthen.
4. Martin Pipe.
5. Jonjo O'Neill.
6. King Charles II (who was nicknamed 'Old Rowley').
7. El Gran Senor (1984).
8. 'Useless'.
9. Harry Carr (who rode Parthia).
10. John Francome.
11. Newmarket.
12. Doug Smith.
13. David O'Brien.

Racing (III)

1. Ballymany Stud, Newbridge, Co. Kildare.
2. The Prix de Diane.
3. John Burke.
4. The Benson and Hedges Gold Cup (York), the Phoenix Champion Stakes (Phoenix Park) and the Dubai Champion Stakes (Newmarket).
5. Just over a furlong from home (240 yards).
6. April the Fifth.
7. Milan.
8. Red Rum.
9. Capt. (later Sir) Cecil Boyd-Rochfort.
10. Fergus A. D'Arcy.
11. Vanton (Jason Titley).
12. Navan.
13. Corals.
14. Dancing Brave.

Racing (IV)

1. Two miles, two furlongs.

2. 200–1.
3. Each has won the American Triple Crown (Kentucky Derby, Belmont Stakes and Preakness Stakes).
4. 1924 (won by Red Splash).
5. Three Troikas.
6. Forty.
7. Won the race by a walk-over.
8. Royal Palace (George Moore).
9. Zongalero.
10. Mill Reef.
11. Steve Cauthen.

Racing (V)

1. Ayr.
2. York.
3. Bonanza Boy.
4. Martell.
5. Nijinsky.
6. Steve Cauthen.
7. Dickens Hill.
8. The 2,000 Guineas.
9. One and a half miles.
10. Arkle.
11. H.H. Aga Khan III.
12. Shergar (1981).
13. The Queen Mother.
14. Bob Champion.

Racing (VI)

1. Three: Down Royal, Downpatrick and Dundalk.
2. The Chair and Water jumps.
3. Vincent O'Brien.
4. Cheltenham.
5. Shoot A Line.

6. Lil E. Tee.
7. Omerta (Mr A. Maguire).
8. Cicero.
9. Rubstic.
10. Bill Williamson.
11. Niniski.
12. Tommy Carmody.
13. Newmarket.

Boxing (I)

1. Sonny Liston.
2. Rocky Marciano.
3. Ken Buchanan.
4. Louisville, Kentucky.
5. Jack Johnson.
6. Los Angeles, 1984.
7. New Orleans.
8. Joe Frazier.
9. Gene Tunney.
10. Billy Conn (Louis won in round thirteen).
11. The (Eighth) Marquess of Queensbury.
12. John L. Sullivan (winner) and Jake Kilrain.
13. Bob Fitzsimmons.

Boxing (II)

1. Tommy Burns.
2. Buddy Baer (Louis won on disqualification in round thirteen).
3. Primo Carnera (Italy) with sixty-nine.
4. Rocky Marciano (who 'knocked out' Jack Dempsey in the final).
5. Jimmy Ellis.
6. Gene Tunney.
7. Archie Moore, USA (at 129).

8. The National Sporting Club.
9. Max Schmeling (winner) and Jack Sharkey.
10. Battling Siki.
11. Archie Moore.
12. Dado Marino, World Flyweight Champion (1950–52), became a grandparent at the age of thirty-four.

Boxing (III)

1. 1975 (1 October).
2. Pascual Perez (in 1954).
3. Jack Dempsey.
4. Thirty-two.
5. It was the first World Heavyweight title fight to be televised.
6. George Foreman.
7. 1979 (27 June).
8. Henry Cooper.
9. Round one (1 m, 31 secs).
10. Evander Holyfield (USA).
11. Havana, Cuba.
12. Max Baer.
13. He was the (5th) Earl of Lonsdale who gave his name to the coveted Lonsdale Belt.
14. Max Schmeling (Heavyweight, 1930).

Boxing (IV)

1. Gus Lesnevich.
2. Jimmy Wilde (also known as the 'Mighty Atom').
3. Danny La Ronde.
4. 11 st. 6 lbs.
5. Three: Welterweight, Light-Middleweight, Light-Heavyweight.
6. Mike McTigue.
7. Jess Williard at 6 ft, 6.25 ins (Carnera was 6 ft, 5.75 ins).
8. Sonny Liston.

9. Leon Spinks.
10. Max Schmeling.
11. Max and Buddy Baer.
12. Paul Pender.
13. Kid Gavilan.

Boxing (V)

1. James J. Braddock (about Joe Louis).
2. Joe Bugner.
3. Cassius Clay (as he was then known).
4. Tony Zale.
5. Middleweight.
6. New York.
7. Welterweight.
8. Middleweight.
9. Ghana.
10. Barney Ross.
11. Lazlo Papp.
12. Bantamweight.
13. Leon and Michael Spinks (Light-Heavyweight and Middleweight respectively).

GAA Football (I)

1. Tyrone (beat Kerry, 4–16 to 1–5).
2. Brian Mullins, Ray Hazley, Ciaran Duff (Dublin), Tomas Tierney (Galway).
3. *Out of Our Skins*.
4. Wexford (1915–18).
5. Paddy Moclair.
6. Cavan (1947).
7. 1935 (Cavan v Kildare — 50,380).
8. Alf Murray (1964).
9. Galway (1–11 to 0–11).
10. Munster (beat Connacht, 2–3 to 0–5).
11. Green and white.

12. Belfast (21–23 April 1984).
13. One point.
14. Roscommon.
15. Laois (1–11 to 0–8).

GAA Football (II)

1. Bryan MacMahon.
2. Down.
3. Cork.
4. Ulster (beat Connacht, 1–12 to 1–7).
5. Paddy Moriarty's.
6. Meath.
7. Tadgh Murphy.
8. Kilkenny (beat Wexford, 1–4 to 0–2).
9. Connacht.
10. At the Polo Grounds, New York, in 1947 when Cavan and Kerry stood to attention for 'A Soldier's Song' and 'The Star-Spangled Banner'.
11. Tony Hanahoe.
12. Kerry.
13. Hugh Duggan.

GAA Football (III)

1. Austin Stacks.
2. For comments on referee Seamus Aldridge's handling of the 1978 All-Ireland Final in an interview with *Magill* magazine.
3. Paudie O'Shea.
4. Dublin 1901–1902.
5. Dr Crokes (Kerry).
6. Cavan (beat Wexford, 1–11 to 1–5).
7. Tony Hanahoe.
8. Dick ('Dickeen') Fitzgerald.
9. 1896.
10. Paddy O'Rourke.

11. Munster (Ulster scored 0–15).
12. Anton O'Toole.
13. Cork.
14. Matt Connor.

GAA Football (IV)

1. Tim Kennelly.
2. Eugene Magee.
3. Twenty-one.
4. Clare.
5. Antrim.
6. Liam Sammon.
7. Con Murphy (Cork).
8. Con Houlihan (*Evening Press*).
9. Bernard Brogan.
10. Armagh (1977).
11. Roscommon (by 0–14 to 0–8).
12. Robbie Kelleher.

GAA Football (V)

1. 'Pat-O'.
2. Jem Roche.
3. Tommy Doyle.
4. New York (it proved to have been only temporarily mislaid).
5. Owen McCann.
6. Johnny Mooney.
7. Joe Lennon.
8. Kerry (winners) and Armagh.
9. James McCartan.
10. Limerick (0–23 to 3–12).
11. Jimmy Keaveney.
12. Seamus Aldridge (Kildare).
13. John Joe Reilly.

GAA Football (VI)

1. John O'Keeffe.
2. Sean Doherty.
3. Monaghan.
4. Dr Mick Loftus.
5. Charlie Nelligan (Kerry) and John McCarthy (Dublin).
6. Eoin Liston (Kerry).
7. Tommy Carr.
8. Dublin (by defeating Galway 1–10 to 1–8).
9. Tipperary.
10. Danny Lynch.
11. Mick Lyons.
12. Jack O'Shea (Kerry).
13. Clann na Gael.
14. Royal Liver Assurance.

Hurling (I)

1. Kilkenny's Minor hurlers.
2. Paddy Scanlan.
3. Pat Delaney.
4. Aeroflot.
5. 1891.
6. Noel Lane.
7. Cloyne.
8. 1938 (beat Clare, 3–5 to 2–5).
9. One (1957).
10. Tommy Doyle.
11. Kilkenny.
12. Pat Fleury (Cork won, 3–16 to 1–12).
13. Galway (beat Clare, 3–12 to 3–10 in the 1986–87 Final).
14. Kevin Matthews.

Hurling (II)

1. Kilkenny ('Drug') and Cork ('Bowler').
2. Michael Cleary (Tipperary).

3. Loughgiel Shamrocks (Antrim).
4. One (1915).
5. Angela Downey.
6. Dan Quigley.
7. Roscrea (Tipperary).
8. Winners of the Oireachtas competition.
9. St Flannan's (Ennis).
10. Eddie Keher (0–10 from frees).
11. Wexford (winners) and Galway.
12. 1953 and '54.
13. Dublin.
14. Dundalk (on the Cooley Mountains).

Hurling (III)

1. 1987.
2. Bernie Hartigan.
3. Seamus J. King.
4. All are Senior All-Ireland dual medal winners.
5. Antrim (beaten by Cork) and Galway (beaten by Offaly).
6. Galway.
7. Semple Stadium, Thurles is named in honour of Tom Semple.
8. Cork (by 1–5 to 0–4).
9. 1914.
10. Twice: 1962 and '65.
11. 1983.
12. Richie Bennis (0–8 from frees).
13. Offaly-born Joe McKenna (who played for Limerick).
14. Tipperary (3–11 to 0–3 in 1949).

Hurling (IV)

1. Congress of 1914.
2. J. Rankins.
3. The winners of the Inter-Varsity Camogie Championship.

4. 1896 (in the replayed game with Dublin who scored 4–6).
5. The passing of Limerick's Mick Mackey.
6. Portlaoise.
7. Wexford.
8. Niall Patterson.
9. Noel Skehan (Kilkenny).
10. Limerick (in 1921).
11. John Fenton.

Hurling (V)

1. Gerry Kirwan (Offaly).
2. Castlegar (1980).
3. Cork (winners) and Wexford.
4. Ollie Walsh.
5. Three (1980, '87 and '88).
6. Seamus Durack (Clare).
7. The Tommy Moore Memorial Trophy.
8. Bryan MacMahon.
9. Michael Maher (Tipperary, 1895, '96 and '98).
10. Rathnure.
11. Sean Og Murphy.
12. Jimmy Smith.
13. The Gaelic League.
14. Five (1941, '42, '43, '44 and '46).
15. Nicky Orr.